MENTAL TOUGHNESS JOURNAL

MENTAL TOUGHNESS JOURNAL
BY FLOW SPORT MENTAL PERFORMANCE COACHING

123 Links Ave, Mount Maunganui, New Zealand

Written by Zane Winslade
Cover and Design by Sprout Marketing
and Inkblot Graphic Design

First edition printed in China through Asia Pacific Offset
Second edition printed by KDP Amazon

ISBN: 978-04-73588-85-4

www.mentaltoughnessjournal.com (International)
www.flowsport.co.nz (NZ)

MENTAL TOUGHNESS IS NOT SOMETHING THAT
YOU EITHER HAVE OR DON'T HAVE.
WE ALL HAVE MENTAL TOUGHNESS WITHIN US.
THIS JOURNAL WILL HELP YOU UNCOVER YOURS.

WELCOME!

A list of what's included in this journal

Congratulations! By picking up this book you've started on a journey that can transform your life and your performance in sport. The pages that follow contain the sequence of exercises that will help inspire huge change in your ability to thrive under stress and pressure. With commitment to the process you can produce the results you've been dreaming of. Many athletes put a lot of effort into getting stronger, faster or more skilful but the top athletes know that training the mind gives you the ultimate edge. That's why taking this first leap and exploring some ways you can improve your mindset is a massive step forward. Well done!

I AM HERE TO HELP!

My name is Zane Winslade from Flow Sport. I am trained and educated in the science of Sport Psychology, and I help performers, both young and old, develop a healthy mindset so they can get the best out of themselves. This journal is designed as a masterclass in some of the foundations you'll need to develop that strong and resilient mind.

WELL DONE ON PICKING UP THIS JOURNAL AND COMMITTING TO BECOMING A MORE RESILIENT PERSON!

Inside the book are some of the mental skills used by the world's top athletes. These skills might just give you the edge you've been looking for. Unlocking the power of your mind will take your performance to the next level and beyond. If you put the time and effort into practising these skills you will become a more calm, confident and mentally tough athlete. That means you'll enjoy your sport more, but it also means you'll be a better person. More importantly, you'll be the person you want to be – the best version of yourself. You'll be able to do this because you won't be restrained by the difficult thoughts and feelings that can hold us back from truly expressing ourselves in the moments that matter.

This journal uses some of the latest research in performance psychology, and is written in a way that is easy to understand and be as practical as possible. So now it's up to you to put it all into practice.

SO WHAT IS MENTAL TOUGHNESS ANYWAY?

Mental Toughness means you are able to remain focused on the task at hand, despite uncomfortable thoughts and feelings. It means you can perform even when you're not feeling good! And it means you don't give up when these feelings arise. Let's be clear though, it doesn't mean you don't ever feel stressed, upset or nervous! It means you don't let those feelings control what you do and how you perform.

Being mentally tough means you can show the following three things:

1. YOU CAN STAY "IN THE PRESENT".
2. YOU HAVE CLEAR VALUES AND GOALS TO GUIDE YOU.
3. YOU CAN COURAGEOUSLY COMMIT TO GIVING YOUR ALL IN THE MOMENT, REGARDLESS OF HOW YOU FEEL.

In a way it's like being flexible. Instead of letting your emotions and unhelpful thoughts control you, you can perform whilst concentrating on the task at hand. You can choose to act in a way that reflects what is important to you. Inside this journal are the tools and exercises designed to help you achieve this.

I AM CONFIDENT THAT THE CONTENTS OF THIS JOURNAL WILL KICK-START MASSIVE GROWTH IN YOURSELF, YOUR SELF-CONFIDENCE AND YOUR ABILITY TO PERFORM UNDER PRESSURE... **HOWEVER,** THERE IS ONE CONDITION! YOU STILL HAVE TO DO THE...

WORK!

You have to commit honestly to doing the exercises that are presented in this book and then use it as often as possible throughout your season. Monitor your progress, check that you are making the small, important changes, and then reflect on your journey and stay focused on your goals. After all, if you want to make real change, you have to take small steps. Every day. That is the most important mental training you can do.

As they say in the US Navy Seals:

"WE DON'T RISE TO THE LEVEL OF OUR EXPECTATIONS, WE SINK TO THE LEVEL OF OUR TRAINING"

KNOWING YOU
"Know yourself, and you will win all battles"
-Lao Tzu

KNOWING YOU

For sport and for life in general, it's a good idea to start thinking about who you are and what is important to you.

THIS IS THE FOUNDATION OF A RESILIENT MINDSET!
IT COMES FROM A PLACE OF KNOWING YOURSELF REALLY WELL.

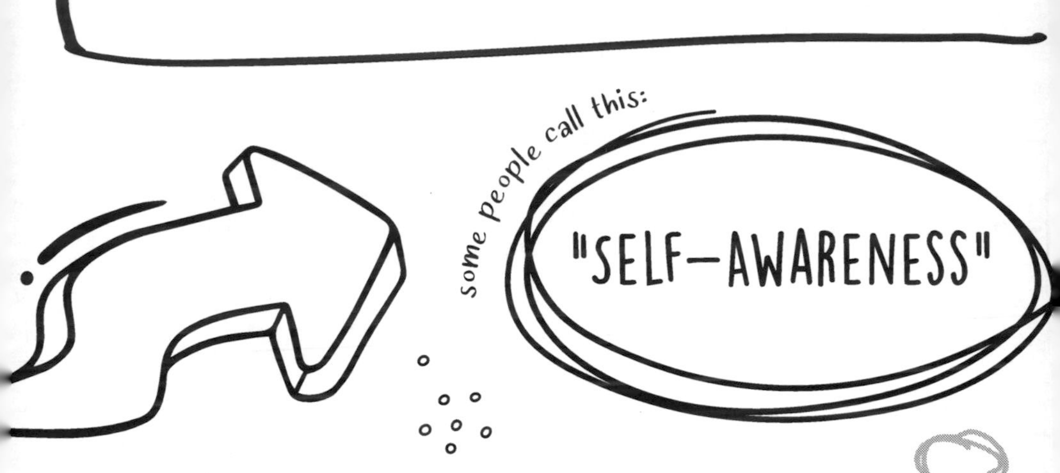

When you know who you are, what you stand for, and most importantly who you want to be, you can really focus on being that person during sports performances and in all other areas of your life too!

It gives you a focus that is more important than any goal. Focusing on being a certain person is powerful because it is something you can always control. It makes you feel better about your life and it helps you make decisions easier.

Goals come and go.
They change a lot throughout our life.
The kind of person you are is more constant, it doesn't change as much as goals do. Who you are is a combination of the things you've experienced and the genes you have inherited.

You are unique in what you can offer the world, and it is important to know those qualities about yourself so you know what you can give to the world. When you are clear on these, success becomes more about how well you expressed yourself. Rather than how well you did, compared to other people.

IT MEANS YOU CAN SAY:

I am not what my mind tells me I am when I'm feeling down.

One of the most important psychological needs for human beings is the need to belong. We are tribal animals. You belong to a family and a long line of ancestors. These people have contributed to who you are today! Now it is time to get clear on your family's history and the stories that have helped create who you are. This is a terrific foundation for Mental Toughness. So complete the following to help you identify a bit more about who you are and where you come from.

I would encourage having some conversations with your family or other important people in your life. These are powerful conversations to have.

Where did my ancestors come from?

What significant things have my ancestors done?

What jobs did they do?

What struggles did they face? What historical events did they live through?

How has my ancestry influenced 'Who I am' today?

Where do I live now and how does that influence what is important to me now?

THE MASKS WE WEAR

"It takes courage to grow up and
turn out to be who you really are"
- E.E. Cumings

THE MASKS WE WEAR

When we think about who we are and our identity, it can helps us to understand ourselves by recognising what 'masks' we wear.

What does this mean? Well, it is like we wear 'masks' that cover different parts of personalities in order show the world something else. This is going on all the time.

These are not actual masks, but ways that we change and hide ourselves depending on the people we are with and the situation we are in. We might be afraid of people seeing a part of us that we are ashamed about or that might make us think we seem weak or not good enough **(although actually it's the opposite – showing the true you is the bravest thing you can do!)**

For example, we wear one mask at home, and another at school.

Similarly, we might wear a mask in sport, and that might be a bit different to who we are at school!

The questions below are about asking about the **YOU** beneath the different masks we wear. I know this can be hard, but try to sit down and have a good think about it. You can always come back to this part if you're having trouble thinking about it right now.

When I am being myself truly, what am I like? Think of some words to describe yourself. What would your best friends say about you?

List some of the things you have done in your life that you're proud of – not just in sport. Think a bit about it and write them down, and then write down why those things make you feel proud. E.g. did you overcome an obstacle, or make a positive difference in someone else's life?

Think about some masks. Who do you sometimes pretend to be but know deep down that it's not really you?

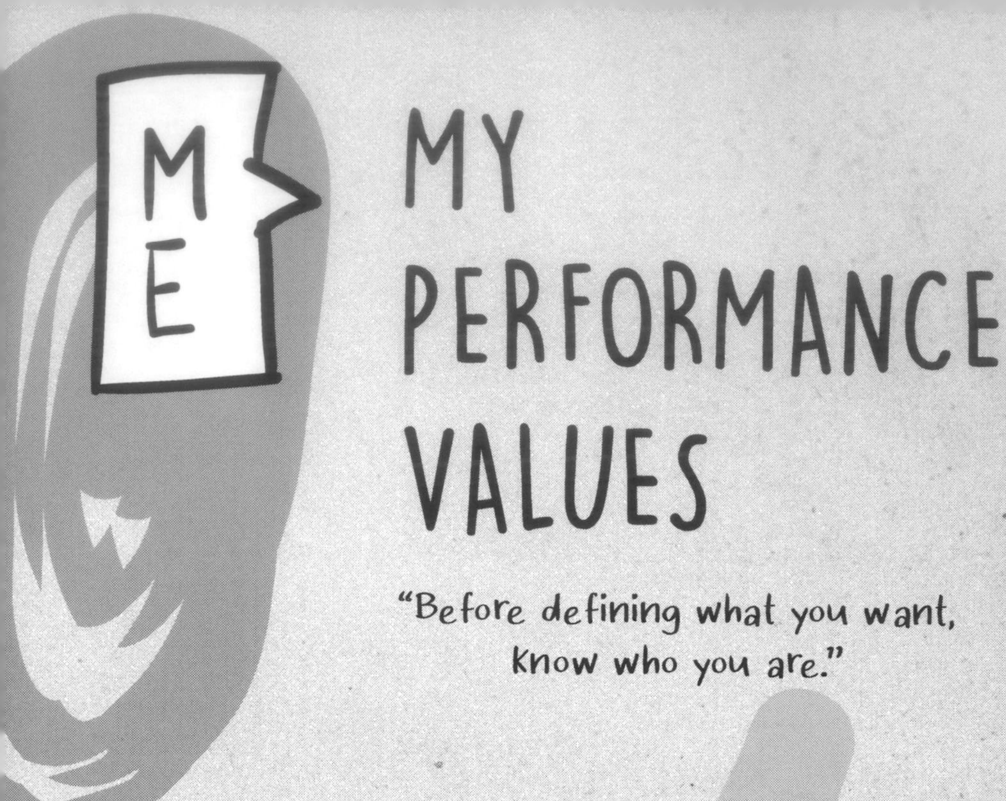

MY PERFORMANCE VALUES

"Before defining what you want,
know who you are."

MY PERFORMANCE VALUES

Now you have had a bit of a think about who you are and who you're not, it's important you go through the descriptions and try and come up with some key words that really summarise who you **WANT** to be.

WE CALL THESE WORDS VALUES, BECAUSE THEY ARE THE WAYS THAT YOU VALUE BEING. THESE ARE UP TO YOU. YOU NEED TO CHOOSE WHAT IS IMPORTANT TO YOU!

HERE'S SOME EXAMPLES:

Do you enjoy and strive to be a kind person, to be a good teammate, or to never give up? These things would show that you really value kindness, teamwork or persistence.

Having clear values is like having a super power. They can make you absolutely clear about what you want to do. Once you have a good set of values up your sleeve, you can then consciously focus on them and make sure they are a part of your life, your performance in sport, and everything you do.

These are great values, because they describe the person you want to be, and what you are going to do, rather than just a thing we want to achieve.

BECAUSE YOU CHOSE THEM, YOU'LL THEN FEEL PRETTY GOOD ABOUT THE DIRECTION YOU ARE HEADING IN WHEN YOU TRY AND LIVE THOSE THINGS AS MUCH AS POSSIBLE.

You can think of them as a guiding compass. When you're stuck and unsure which way to go, you can look at your values and decide who you need to be in any moment.

Then at the end of the day you can say to yourself:

"I am glad I was the person I wanted to be today, and I didn't change because of the circumstances"

Below are some words that might help the process for you. You may have some of these exact words, or similar, already. After answering the questions on the previous page you might struggle to put some of it into the right words.

PICK SOME BELOW THAT REALLY SUM UP THE PERSON WHO YOU'D LIKE TO BE.

Start by circling the ones that are most important to you, then cross out the rest. Next, try and narrow it down to five or less. Only leave ones that are the **MOST** important.

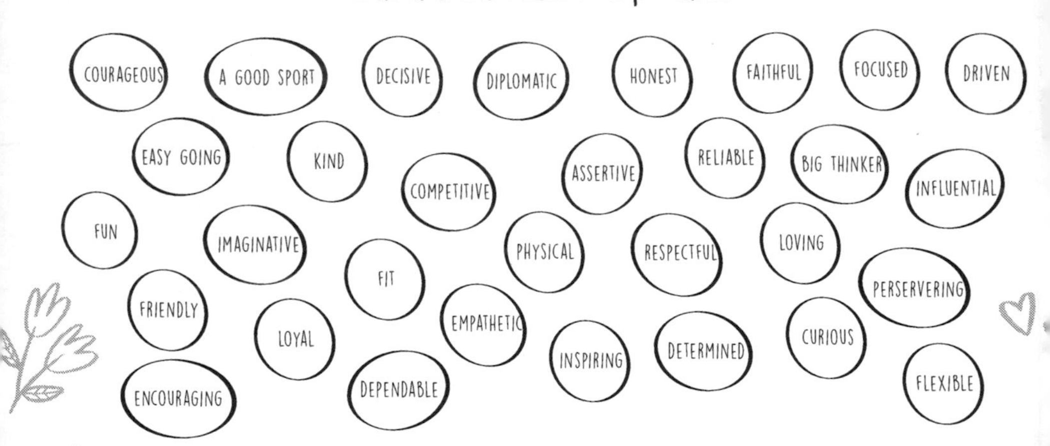

GREAT! YOU SHOULD NOW HAVE SOME WORDS THAT REALLY SUMMARISE THE PERSON YOU WOULD LIKE TO BE.

TEST THEM OUT

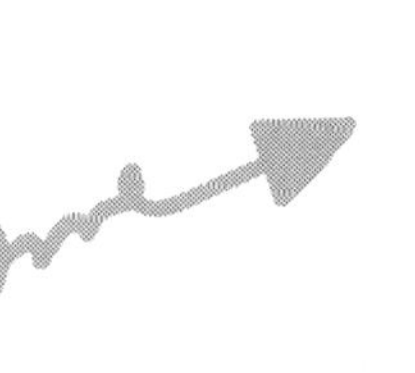

Take a moment to close your eyes and imagine yourself at an older age. Picture yourself at a retirement dinner, where you are being honoured for everything you have done. Your friends, teammates or colleagues have aged, so there is a lot more grey hair than now! Perhaps you have been involved in the sport (or maybe it's just a job that you dedicated yourself to) for a long period of time and you are at a function to honour this service. Many people stand up to speak about you; they say all sorts of things about what you have achieved, all the wins and the personal milestones and achievements. You can imagine these things if you'd like! But then, even more importantly, what do you imagine them saying about who you are as a person?

THIS EXERCISE IS A GREAT WAY TO UNCOVER WHETHER WE HAVE A TRUE PICTURE OF THE TYPE OF PERSON WE WANT TO BE.

If you're thinking it'd be great if they talked about the exact things you've already identified, then that's great! You nailed it! But, if you imagined them saying some other things about yourself, that's OK too. Now is the time to really think about what positive things you would want people to say and then put them onto the list. See if they would take the place of the current value words that you already have.

YOU CAN ALSO NOTICE AND ASSESS HOW WELL YOU ARE DOING AT LIVING THESE THINGS RIGHT NOW.

WRITE DOWN YOUR PERFORMANCE VALUES BELOW

(this is the person who I want to be!)

You can use pictures as well!

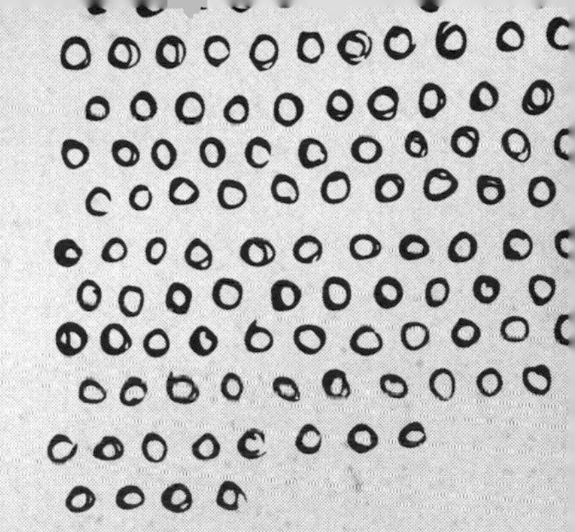

YOUR GOALS

"The greater danger for most of us isn't that our aim is too high and we miss it, but that it is too low and we reach it."

- Michelango

WE LIVE IN A WORLD OF EXCESSIVE GOAL-SETTING!

WARNING:

GOALS

Everyone is being forced to think about being better and better at everything we do. This is causing a lot of people to get upset! They feel like they never keep up or achieve the goals they should be achieving.

SO, ALTHOUGH SETTING GOALS IS VERY IMPORTANT, IT'S ALSO IMPORTANT WE REALISE THAT LIFE IS HAPPENING RIGHT NOW, ALL THE TIME, AND WE CAN STILL ENJOY THE MOMENTS WE ARE IN.

It can make people feel like they aren't good enough or that they aren't doing enough to achieve goals.

We have moments all the time where we can be fulfilled by doing things that are important to us. We can "smell the roses" and enjoy the moment. Enjoying the process of getting better and better is the real trick! It's great to be on the journey; you don't always have to be dreaming about being at a certain destination.

SO REMEMBER THESE HARMFUL SIDES TO GOAL-SETTING:

You might always feel like you need to be someplace else, rather than being comfortable being on the journey.

It can make people feel like they aren't good enough or that they aren't doing enough to achieve goals.

You might only focus on the goal, and then change who you are because you think it will help you get there quicker. (This will make you feel worse in the long term!)

Also, be careful: it might not be a goal that YOU want; it might be just what your parents, coaches or friends expect of you.

Many athletes dedicate their life to sport and achieve great things, but then feel empty or depressed when they achieve all their goals. Crazy, huh?!

STAY TRUE TO YOU

Sometimes it's because they have forgotten who they are and what is important to them along the way. Life became about results and nothing else.

Their identity got tied up and confused with what they wanted to achieve. So when they achieved those things, they realised that they still didn't feel fulfilled. I mean, they might realise that winning is great at first, and be really happy and have a big party after winning, but a few days later they are back to the same life. Achieving a goal doesn't miraculously create endless happiness. That's why we need to have more to us than just goals!

NOW LET'S TALK ABOUT THE GOOD STUFF:

Goals give you direction and help you stay motivated.

Goals can help you build confidence by making you feel like you have a plan.

Goals can help you build confidence when you tick them off!

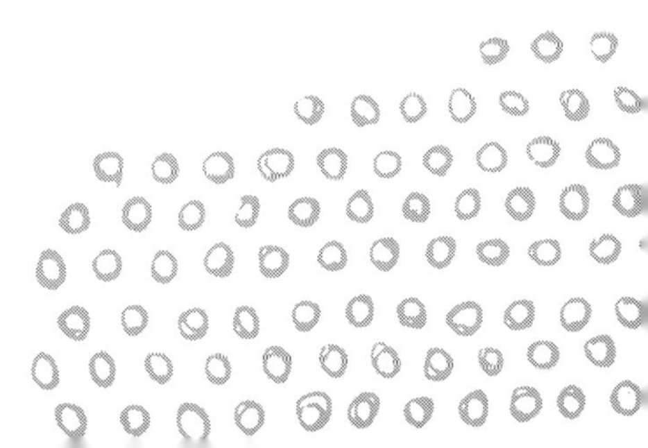

YOUR GOALS

"IF YOU AIM FOR NOTHING, YOU'LL HIT IT EVERY TIME."

With goal-setting, it is important we start big and then work our way down. So let's start with the **ultimate dream goal.** This might be the one you might feel a little bit embarrassed telling others about because it's so far off and might seem unbelievable to them! Once you've identified that, then work your way down.

GREAT Those goals are going to be awesome for you to aim for. But, chances are they are not "How I am going to get better" goals.

They are likely places you want to get to, or results, or teams you want to be in.

So now you know the direction and places you want to go, start to think about what you can start doing over the next month (and then repeat every month) that will take you closer. What are some habits or actions you could take on a regular basis to help you achieve your goal?

OK

THESE WOULD BE THINGS LIKE:

"extra left-hand passing practice 4 times per week at 7pm every evening for 10 minutes, for the next month"

See how specific that is? It's something you can achieve that helps with your journey, not just a place you want to be in the future. It's about steps to get somewhere. But the good thing is, we still feel really satisfied when we achieve these goals, and they help us build confidence.

(It's often called a Process Goal, Because you aim to put your energy into the process rather than the outcomes.)

Give it a go: "I can get better by doing ...."

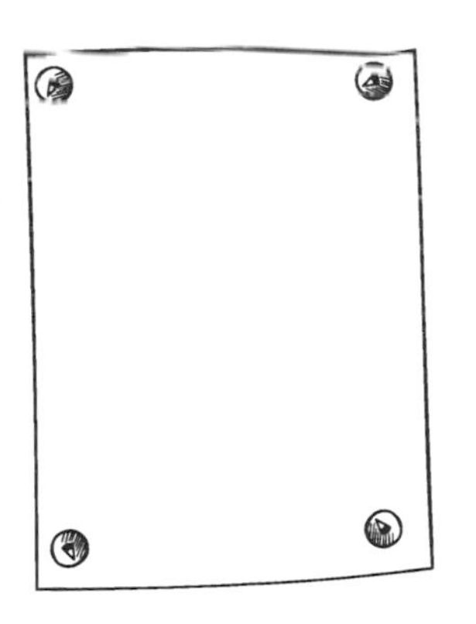

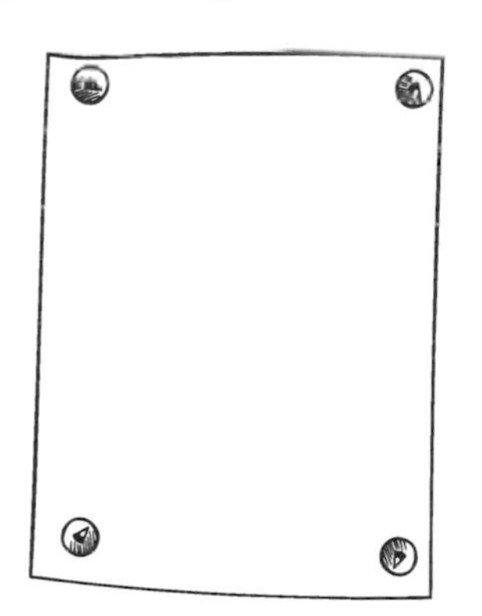

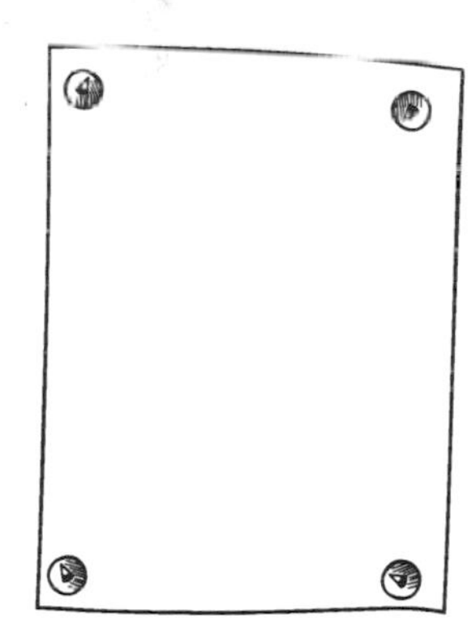

THE BIG OBSTACLES

“The greater the obstacle, the more glory in overcoming it.” - Moliére

There are always obstacles that can get in the way of us achieving what we want to achieve. If there weren't, then the goals would probably be too easy!

So now is the time to think about yourself, and try and predict what habits you currently have that will potentially get in the way of you achieving your goals. You can also think about other obstacles that can slow you down or hold you back. Some of these things we will have very little control over, and some things we will have complete control over.

THE MOST IMPORTANT THINGS TO CONSIDER ARE THE THINGS THAT YOU KNOW ABOUT YOURSELF THAT CAN GET IN THE WAY.

Like, do you struggle to get up in the morning for training? Do you lose motivation easily? Do you avoid situations because you get nervous? Do you forget equipment that is necessary for training? Do you eat unhealthy foods? Fill in the blanks with the obstacles that get in the way of your goals!

MY BIG OBSTACLES:

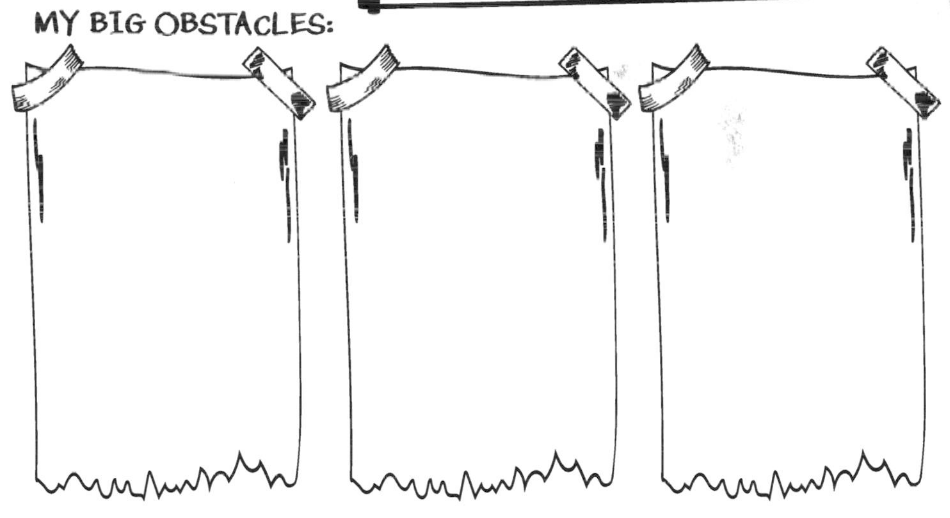

THINK ABOUT WHAT YOU WILL NEED TO DO IN ORDER TO STOP THOSE OBSTACLES FROM HOLDING YOU BACK.

A lot of the other resources in this book will help you deal with these obstacles, but there may be some other practical steps you can take to make sure the obstacles don't become roadblocks. You might be able to plan ahead and prevent some of these obstacles having such a big effect on you and what you want to achieve.

SOME THINGS I CAN START DOING RIGHT NOW, SOME THINGS I CAN KEEP DOING, AND SOME THINGS I NEED TO STOP DOING.

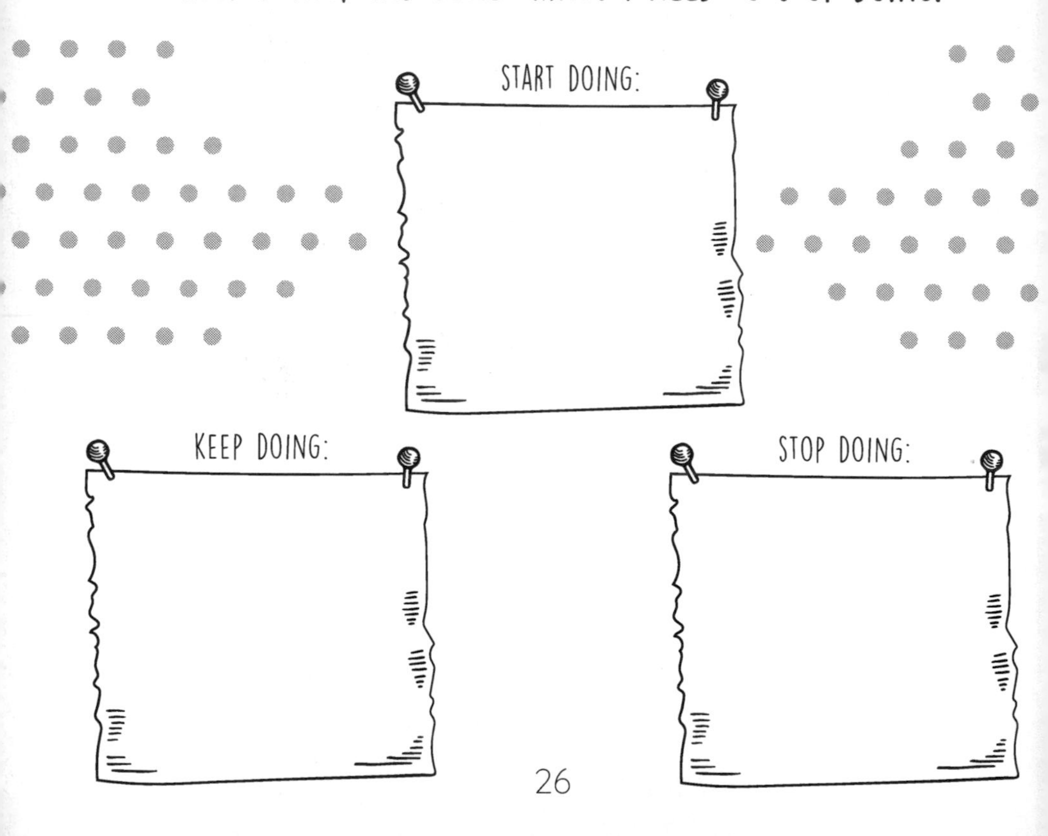

COURAGE AND THE CHALLENGE MINDSET

"Fear is a reaction, Courage is a decision."

- Winston Churchill

CHALLENGE MINDSET

The key to developing mental toughness is being able to take difficult but important steps forward, while being willing to experience discomfort. That often means deliberately doing that which makes you uncomfortable. A lot of the time the reason it makes you nervous or worried is because you care about it. So often the fact that you experience discomfort can indicate you are doing something that fits nicely with your values and goals.

I call this the "Challenge Mindset", because it means you see the discomfort as a challenge rather than a threat or a thing to avoid and run away from.

That means if something is really hard and is going to make us uncomfortable, we can use a challenge mindset and recognise that it is something good, because it tests us, helps us grow and is likely very important to who we are, what we value, and the goals we have.

CHALLENGE MINDSET MANTRA: THE BEST THINGS WE DO WILL PROBABLY BE THE HARDEST THINGS WE DO!

Think about it like this: When we train our body, we know we have to make it uncomfortable to become fit and strong. Sometimes training hurts! It is like that with our brains as well as our bodies.

Every day we make decisions to make us feel better and comfortable instantly – or alternatively, we take uncomfortable steps forward that will make us feel better about ourselves in the longer term.

FOR EXAMPLE, IF YOU GET UP AND DO SOME EXERCISE, THAT MIGHT BE A BIT UNCOMFORTABLE IF YOU PUSH YOURSELF HARD, BUT AFTERWARDS YOU WILL FEEL GREAT THAT YOU HAVE DONE IT!

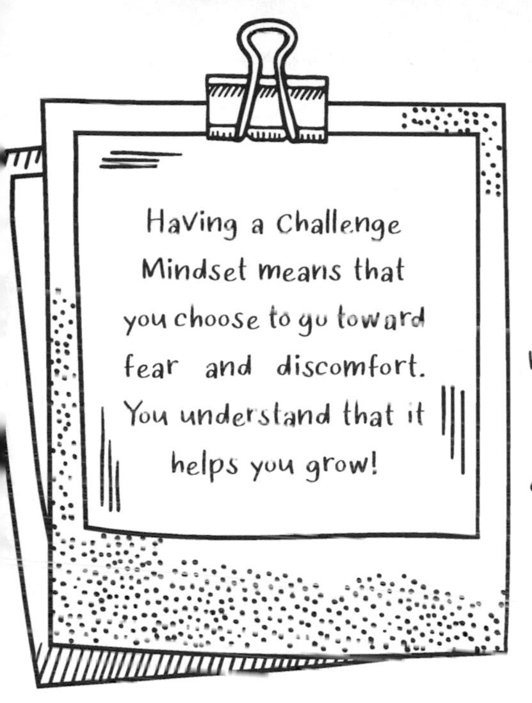

The opposite is where we choose the easier option that makes us feel good instantly, but feel worse in the long run. This is where you avoid doing the right thing because it makes you uncomfortable. Avoiding discomfort makes you feel good instantly. But the long term effect can be harmful. For example, you have an important assignment to do for school in a subject that is important to you. You may be tempted to put it off and avoid working on it because doing it is tiring and time consuming. So you choose to spend time on your phone looking at Instagram or something else. Doing that feels better because it's easier and distracts you from the hard things you could be doing. The downside is that you will likely feel worse the next day, when you realise you haven't done any more of the assignment! You chose to avoid discomfort rather than being willing to experience it whilst doing the thing that is important to you.

BECAUSE YOU DON'T MAKE A STEPS FORWARD YOU BEGIN TO FEEL WORSE ABOUT YOURSELF, EVEN THOUGH YOU FELT GOOD INSTANTLY AFTER AVOIDING DISCOMFORT. THE LONG-TERM FEELING IS ONE OF REGRET AND GUILT.

If we constantly chase things that make us avoid feeling uncomfortable in the moment, then we won't feel as good about where we are going in the long term.

Now this can go the other way too. For example, if we ONLY take actions based on what will make us better in the long term then we might get burnt out and tired because we haven't let ourselves relax and be accepting of where we are on our journey. People can become perfectionists and forget to enjoy the small things in life. So make sure to take time to relax and do things that give you some instant enjoyment. The decisions that will make you mentally tougher are when you choose to act on a value, despite the urge to avoid doing it.

Review your goals and values from the first two sections. Identify the avoiding that will get in the way of you living how you want, being who you are and achieving what you want to achieve.

"THE HARDER THE CLIMB, THE BETTER THE VIEW"

Here's another example.

Let's say you know that you don't like to speak up at school but you have the goal of being a leader in a team, or being an influential person is important to you. Now, the more times you can embrace and be willing to have the fear and discomfort of speaking up at school, the better you will get at communicating. You will gain confidence, improve, and be able to achieve your goal. You take the action that is **HARD** and you begin to feel more confident. It's proven to work!

Now, remember, don't expect this to feel good in the actual moment. You might be really nervous and uncomfortable, and your mind might be saying "don't do it!"

So you need to be aware of how you might be wanting to avoid these feelings and be drawn to what feels safer and easier. This would be to avoid the hard thing – the opposite of courage. So when you choose to avoid, you feel instantly relieved and glad you didn't have to feel the uncomfortable feelings of fear and embarrassment... **BUT**, this would not take you closer to your goals, AND you might not be living your values, AND it would make the fear and discomfort even worse in the future! It would be like taking a backwards step with your confidence. It is true that sometimes things won't go well. That is OK too. You are likely to make mistakes and slip up. That's where you can remind yourself that you are not perfect and that is OK.

So, this is where the challenge mindset and the courage comes in. The more times you can make courageous decisions that support the direction of your goals and values, the better you will feel in the future and the more likely you will be to achieve your goals and get through your obstacles.

SO, TAKING IN MIND THE **OBSTACLES** YOU HAVE IDENTIFIED, THINK ABOUT SOME OF THE UNCOMFORTABLE FEELINGS YOU MIGHT HAVE TO EXPERIENCE WITH A **CHALLENGE MINDSET** INSTEAD OF THE AVOIDANCE MINDSET.

Do remember: We can still enjoy the occasional thing that gives us pleasure straight away.

WRITE DOWN SOME OF THE UNCOMFORTABLE FEELINGS YOU MIGHT HAVE WHEN GOING THROUGH THE HARDER TIMES:

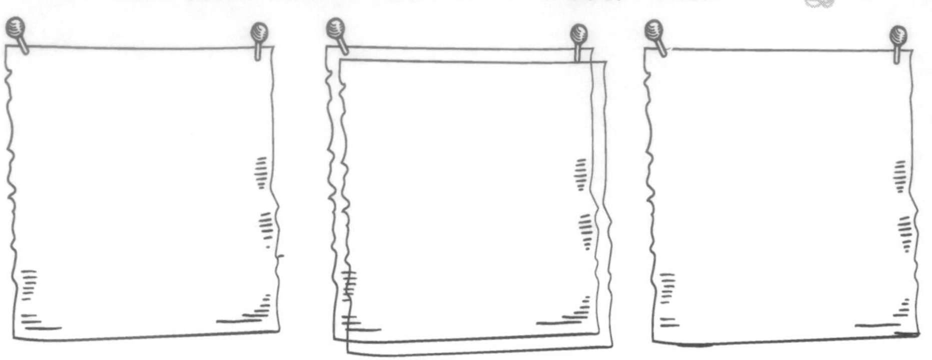

Now think about what your mind might say before you do something hard or uncomfortable. Check out the table below and add some of your own ones! On the right you will see how we can say something different to ourselves when we notice our mind saying these things!

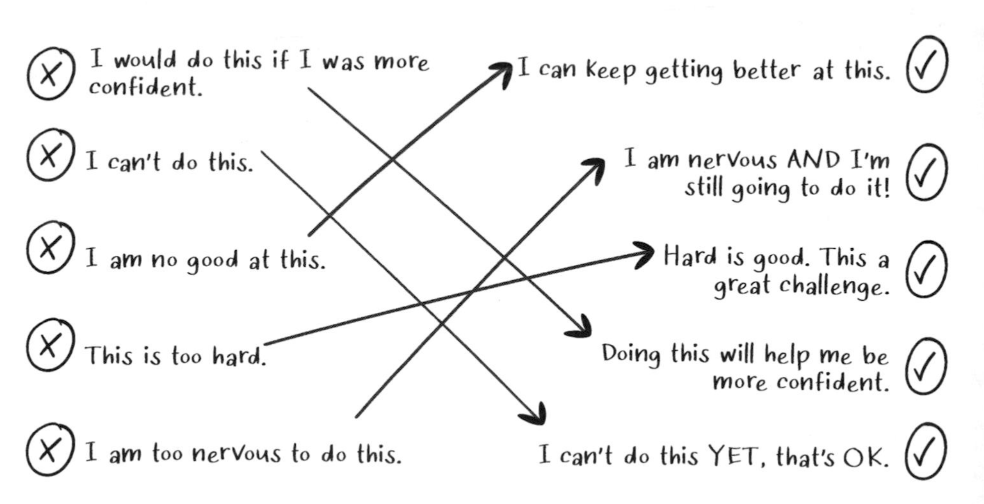

TAKING ON OBSTACLES AND THE UNCOMFORTABLE FEELINGS THEY MIGHT BRING

Think about these as acts of courage, because doing the right thing when there is an easier option is a courageous act! Choosing something uncomfortable is hard! **Be brave!**

THINK OF IT LIKE THIS:
Every time we do something courageous, it's like depositing money into a bank account. It will grow over time the more savings you make. Let's call it the brave bank account.

That's why we want to do it. We want to chase hard things because then we get better and better at being uncomfortable. If we are better at being uncomfortable then we are better at dealing with all of the issues and problems that we experience in Sport and in Life.

I'M OKAY

EVERY TIME YOU ACT WITH BRAVERY AND COURAGE YOU GIVE YOURSELF SOME SAVINGS TO FALL BACK ON. BY ACTING THIS WAY YOU SEND A MESSAGE TO YOUR BRAIN, SAYING THESE GOALS AND VALUES ARE SO IMPORTANT TO ME, AND THE CHANCE TO FEEL GOOD INSTANTLY IS NOT GOING TO STOP ME MOVING FORWARD THROUGH THE DISCOMFORT.

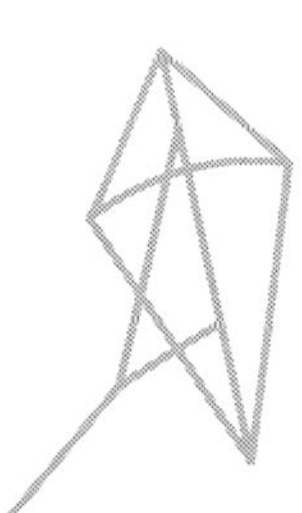

You tell your brain that you are courageous, that you love challenges, and every time uncomfortable feelings come up, you see them as a great big challenge and not as something to run away from.

Every day in this journal has a space for you to write down some courageous steps you can take for the day. Here you can plan and identify some of these important actions that you take. It might help to think about the things that you have worried about or that you might have avoided doing in the past. Here you would write them down and then go and get them done!

IDENTIFY THEM, SHOW YOUR COURAGE AND GO TOWARDS THEM. LOVE THE CHALLENGE! TICKING THEM OFF AT THE END OF THE DAY WILL FEEL AMAZING.

If you don't achieve those in the day (for whatever reason), that's OK too. Everybody slips up! Forgive yourself; be kind to yourself.

Just set some more targets for the next day; think and note down why you didn't get it done, and continue to move forward with courage.

THE BRAVE BANK

I bet there are times you have been really brave in your life – times when you've felt worried, scared or nervous about doing something, and you still managed to be brave and do it anyway!

You need to remember these times and be proud of them! Put them in your brave bank! So you can go back to them and remember those times. Also, make sure you keep adding to it!

REMEMBER, EVERY TIME YOU SHOW COURAGE IT'S LIKE A DEPOSIT IN THE BRAVE BANK ACCOUNT! YOU ARE LITERALLY BUILDING MENTAL TOUGHNESS.

Write in here some of the times you have shown courage in your life.

IMPORTANT POINT:

Taking courageous actions is what should be considered success, because it is the only thing you can control. You can't always control the outcome of whatever you are doing, so make courageous actions the measure of your success!

If, for example, your courageous act was to volunteer to speak at school, don't pay attention too much to how you did in that particular speaking opportunity; you'll do your best with what you've got to give in that moment.

The real success is choosing to be courageous and go towards something that you might have been afraid of. When you choose to do something hard, then you are getting mentally stronger! This is much more important than how well you did at it.

SO, YOU CAN ONLY REALLY FAIL IF YOU CHOOSE TO AVOID THE FEAR AND NOT DO ANYTHING THAT MOVES YOU TOWARDS DISCOMFORT.

SO GO FOR IT!

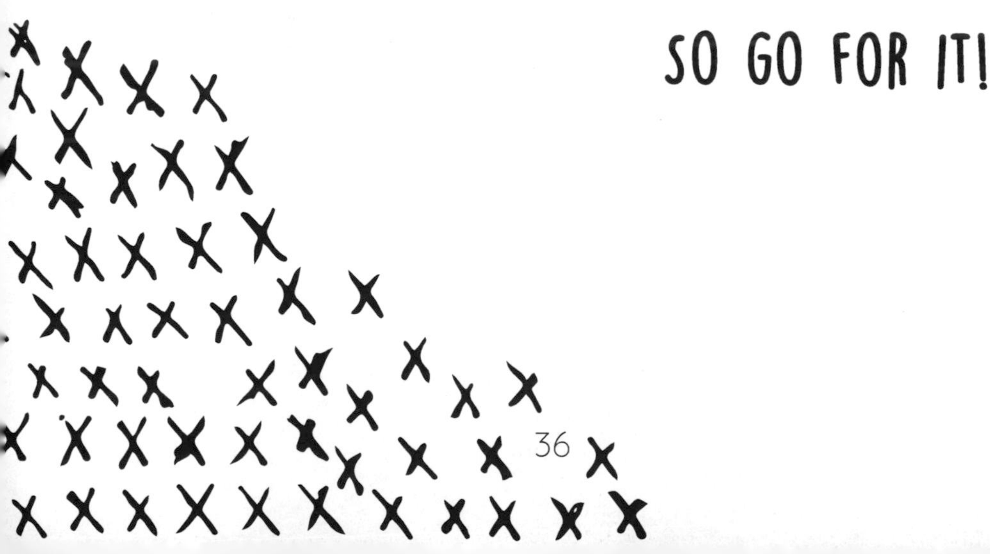

DEALING WITH THE WORRIES, FEARS, DOUBTS (WFDS)

"Worrying is like a rocking chair: it gives you something to do, but never gets you anywhere"

- Erma Bombeck

WFDS

Here's some news that you might not want to hear. Unfortunately, as a human being it is almost guaranteed that you will worry about stuff. Unfair, I know! But just remember that it's OK and a perfectly normal part of life. This is what our brains do. We are equipped with the best worry machines.

We have a powerful imagination, but it also can be very annoying. We can creatively imagine what might happen in the future if we chose to take certain actions. This also means we have a tendency to imagine threats that might hurt us and it is often very unlikely that these bad events will actually happen. But sometimes we can't stop thinking about it!

It's OK!

This is our brain trying to keep us safe by worrying about all the different ways we could end up embarrassed, hurt, isolated or upset. Our brain does not want us to get hurt. I want to encourage you to be OK with your worries. Welcome them in and be willing to accept that they are part of the experience. Let's not make them the enemy.

NOTICE THE WORRYING AND TRY SEPARATING FROM THEM LIKE THIS:

YOU COULD ALSO TRY TO REPEAT THE WORRIES BACK TO YOURSELF IN A FUNNY VOICE, OR SMILE AND THANK YOUR MIND.

But be aware, we are being playful and curious with our thoughts andwhat our mind says to us. We're not mocking and teasing ourselves. We should acknowledge that our mind is doing its thing, and that the story that your mind is telling you in that moment is not helpful. So let's just let go of it.

These thoughts are only harmful if we spend a lot of energy trying to get rid of them, if we become afraid of them or worry about having them.

Avoiding any situations that MIGHT make us feel uncomfortable can have a much more damaging effect in the long term. So if we can put our worries to the side through the exercises above, then we can keep moving forward and doing what we need to do.

REMEMBER, IT'S OK TO WORRY ABOUT THINGS, IT'S NOT NICE, BUT IT'S OK.

ALSO REMEMBER: SOMETIMES WORRIES ARE HELPFUL. LIKE IF WE WERE TO WORRY ABOUT HOW WE WERE GOING TO DO IN A TEST, THEN THAT MIGHT TELL US THAT WE NEED TO DO MORE STUDYING! OTHER TIMES THEY ARE UNHELPFUL, ESPECIALLY WHEN THEY ARE ABOUT THINGS WE CAN'T CONTROL, LIKE WHETHER OR NOT YOU WILL WIN A GAME OR A RACE.

We can't control what other people do, so winning is not really something we can completely control. We can only do our best. We also can't control the opinions other people have of us, what the weather is doing, the tides, the position of the moon, the force of gravity, etc. (You get the picture!)

WRITING DOWN OUR WORRIES

It is really helpful to write down some of the things that you worry about before you go out and perform in your sport.

Try and get it all out by writing down all the things you worry about and fear before you go and compete, even if it seems a bit silly. Through the process of writing these down, you are able to look at them and then hopefully begin to understand how we can notice our worries and take a step back from them. When we can do that, we are able to decide whether or not they are helpful for us in this moment. Try the exercise on the next page!

Notice them but don't necessarily believe them. Remember, our minds like to imagine the worst-case scenarios.

DEALING WITH WORRIES

and choosing actions

LET'S PICK ONE "WORRY" THAT YOU'VE NOTICED YOUR MIND SAYING. NOW WE CAN PRACTICE MANAGING IT IN A HEALTHY WAY: WRITE DOWN WHAT YOUR MIND TELLS YOU HERE:

IS IT HELPFUL?

What can you do right now to act or plan to act on this helpful worry?

Identify it! Say it back to yourself: I am worrying about: ...and that's OK

Re-focus on something you CAN do right now. Let the worry sit there. It only becomes worse if you try to fight it off

WRITE DOWN WORRIES, FEARS AND DOUBTS!

What other things do you worry about in sport? Write them all down!

IT CAN BE HELPFUL TO SEE WHAT IS CONTROLLABLE AND WHAT ISN'T!
SO USE THIS BELOW TO PUT THE WORRIES INTO A CATEGORY:

YOUR MIND IS TRYING TO KEEP YOU SAFE. SO LET IT DO IT'S THING. THE WORRIES WILL BECOME WORSE IF YOU GET INTO A FIGHT WITH THEM. NOTICE THEM, LET THEM BE THERE AND CHOSE AN IMPORTANT VALUE TO FOCUS ON.

MIND-TRAINING ACTIVITIES

"We are what we repeatedly do.
Excellence, therefore, is not an act, but a habit."

-Aristotle

The following chapter gives you some powerful ways you can train your mind on a regular basis (all the other content in the book helps too!). But these activities are skills that you can work on every day to help you get mentally tougher.

IT TAKES A DEEP COMMITMENT TO CHANGE AND AN EVEN DEEPER COMMITMENT TO GROW. – RALPH ELLISON

VISUALISATION

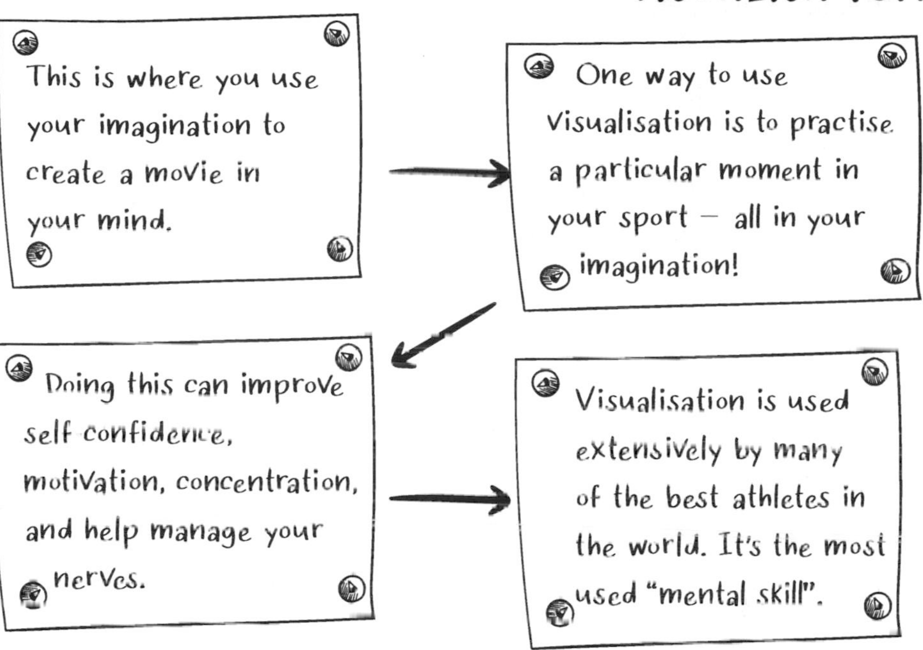

KEEN TO GIVE IT A TRY? FOLLOW THESE STEPS BELOW:

Take a few deep breaths through your nose to relax. → Try and imagine the scene where you will perform. Include all the senses – what you can see, feel, hear, etc. → Re-create what you want to happen – in real time if possible.

"I NEVER HIT A SHOT EVEN IN PRACTICE WITHOUT HAVING A SHARP IN-FOCUS PICTURE OF IT IN MY HEAD. IT'S LIKE A COLOUR MOVIE. FIRST, I 'SEE' THE BALL WHERE I WANT IT TO FINISH, NICE AND WHITE AND SITTING UP HIGH ON THE BRIGHT GREEN GRASS. THEN THE SCENE QUICKLY CHANGES, AND I 'SEE' THE BALL GOING THERE: ITS PATH, TRAJECTORY, AND SHAPE, EVEN ITS BEHAVIOUR ON LANDING. THEN THERE'S A SORT OF FADE-OUT, AND THE NEXT SCENE SHOWS ME MAKING THE KIND OF SWING THAT WILL TURN THE PREVIOUS IMAGES INTO REALITY AND ONLY AT THE END OF THIS SHORT PRIVATE HOLLYWOOD SPECTACULAR DO I SELECT A CLUB AND STEP UP TO THE BALL."

– JACK NICKLAUS (PROFESSIONAL GOLFER)

WHAT ABOUT WHEN THINGS GO WRONG?

Another powerful way to use visualisation is to imagine things going wrong and practising a positive way to respond. It helps to have a plan for things that might go wrong so you feel prepared and ready for anything!

IF YOU COMPETE IN SWIMMING, YOU MIGHT IMAGINE YOUR GOGGLES FALLING OFF AT THE START OF THE RACE AND YOU COULD THEN COME UP WITH A GREAT PLAN TO CONTINUE SWIMMING AT YOUR BEST.

IF YOU COMPETE IN A TEAM SPORT LIKE RUGBY, YOU MIGHT IMAGINE MAKING A MISTAKE EARLY ON IN THE GAME AND REHEARSE SOME POSITIVE WAYS YOU WOULD RESPOND.

IF YOU WERE AN EQUESTRIAN RIDER, YOU MIGHT IMAGINE SOMETHING GOING WRONG AND RESPONDING TO THE HORSE IN A POSITIVE AND CONTROLLED MANNER SO AS TO GET THE MOST OUT OF IT.

MORE TIPS TO HELP WITH YOUR VISUALISING:

Try writing down a script of what you want to imagine, and record yourself reading it. Then you can listen to it before performing.

You can use video to help you picture the images you want in your mind.

DEALING WITH DISTRACTIONS

It's understandable to want to perform with no distractions at all. However, the reality is different. When we compete in sport we often have to deal with distractions that can throw us off our game. It can be helpful to have a bit of a plan on how to deal with them.

DISTRACTIONS CAN ACTUALLY BE IN TWO DIFFERENT TYPES

THEY CAN BE INSIDE OUR OWN HEAD (I.E. WHAT WE THINK AND FEEL).

THEY CAN BE OUTSIDE (I.E. EXTERNAL THINGS LIKE THE WEATHER OR CROWD NOISES).

Believe it or not, both of these types of distractions are actually uncontrollable. Once a thought or a feeling comes up, it's there! We can't magically stop feeling a certain way or stop thinking a thought, especially if spend all our energy trying to get rid of it. What we can do is we can choose to direct our attention to a different task or an external cue. So really it is all about re-focusing our attention on to important tasks, rather than just focusing all the time. Below are a few ways to deal with some of the **distractions** that might come up.

IN YOUR HEAD

- ACKNOWLEDGE THE THOUGHT OR FEELING. SAY 'THANKS MIND'. BRING YOUR ATTENTION BACK TO A KEY CUE WORD OR THE EXTERNAL ENVIRONMENT.
- SNAP! USE A WRISTBAND OR YOUR HAND TO SNAP OR CLAP AGAINST YOUR SKIN TO PHYSICALLY "SNAP" OUT OF IT.

OUTSIDE YOUR HEAD

- PRACTISE IN ADVANCE WITH SOME OF THE DISTRACTIONS THAT MIGHT HAPPEN
- ACCEPT IT FOR HOW IT IS. YOU CAN'T CHANGE IT. YOU CAN ONLY FOCUS ON WHAT YOU CAN CONTROL. REMIND YOURSELF OF WHAT YOU CAN CONTROL.

MY PERFORMANCE PLAN

THE FOLLOWING IS A GREAT PLANNING ACTIVITY TO GO THROUGH BEFORE A BIG COMPETITION. YOU CAN HAVE A MENTAL GAME PLAN! USE ALL THE THINGS FROM THE JOURNAL THAT YOU THINK WOULD BE USEFUL FOR YOU.

FIRST (AS ALWAYS) IDENTIFY WHAT IS MOST IMPORTANT TO YOU. THIS IS NOT HOW WELL YOU WANT TO DO, BUT WHAT KIND OF PERSON YOU WANT TO BE!

SO, TAKE TIME TO CLARIFY: WHAT VALUES ARE YOU GOING TO FOCUS ON DURING THIS GAME OR COMPETITION?

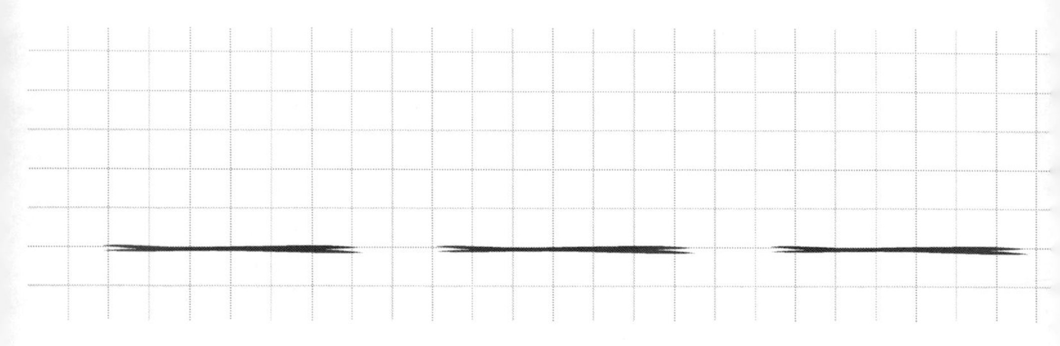

NOW HAVE A THINK ABOUT THE THINGS THAT COULD GO WRONG, THE THINGS YOU CAN DO TO PREPARE FOR THAT, THE WAYS YOU CAN COPE WITH IT IN THE MOMENT!

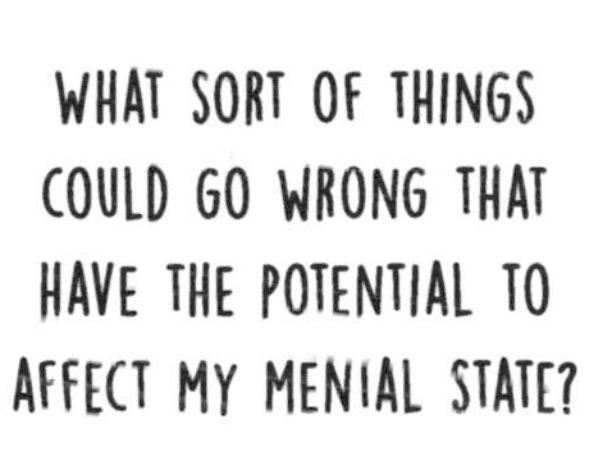

WHAT SORT OF THINGS COULD GO WRONG THAT HAVE THE POTENTIAL TO AFFECT MY MENIAL STATE?

E.g. Making some mistakes right at the start.

WHAT CAN I DO BEFORE MY COMPETITION SO I AM PREPARED FOR THIS?

E.g. Visualise a plan for how I can recover well. Practise anchor-breathing to be able to reset.

WHAT CAN I DO IN THE MOMENT TO COPE BETTER?

E.g. Use anchor breathing to reset. Remind myself of performance values and bring them to life. Remind myself of my plan to recover.

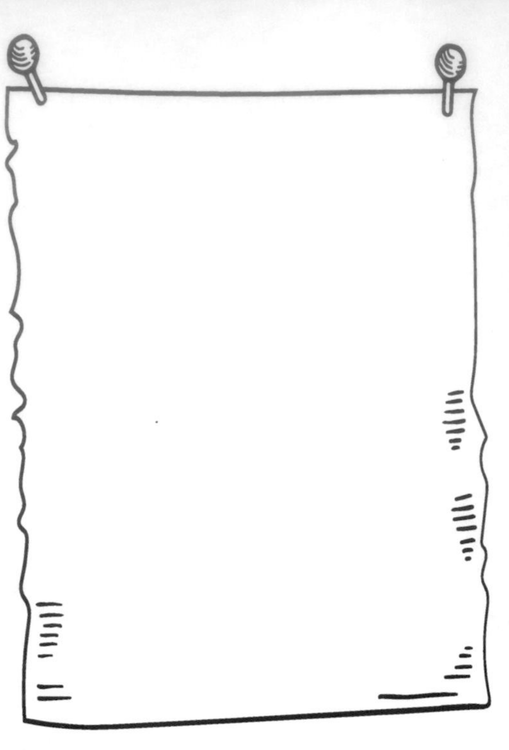

WHAT WILL I DO AFTER MY COMPETITION TO LEARN AND BE EVEN BETTER?

E.g. Write down all the things that went well and worked or talk to my coach or mentor about it.

SLEEP LIKE A CHAMPION!

Did you know that sleep is one of the most important things you can do for your physical and mental health?

SLEEP CAN HELP YOUR MUSCLES ADAPT TO TRAINING BETTER SO YOU'LL BE FASTER, STRONGER OR HAVE MORE ENDURANCE WHEN IT MATTERS.

SLEEP WILL HELP WITH YOUR LEARNING, YOU'LL BE ABLE TO REMEMBER MORE AND THEREFORE BE BETTER ON THE SPORTS FIELD AND IN THE CLASSROOM.

YOU'LL RECOVER BETTER AFTER INTENSE PHYSICAL ACTIVITY AND BE ABLE TO BOUNCE BACK STRONGER AFTER INJURIES.

WITH BETTER SLEEP YOU'LL BE IN A BETTER MOOD MORE OFTEN AND FEEL LESS STRESSED THROUGHOUT THE DAY.

WITH BETTER SLEEP YOU'LL BE ABLE TO FOCUS BETTER AND KEEP A CLEAR HEAD ON THE SPORTS FIELD.

Here are some tips on helping you get the most out of your sleep:

- Wind down: In the evening, close to bed time, do some relaxing activities that aren't too physical or stressful. E.g. reading a book is a great activity to wind down.
- Avoid bright lights: Your brain will see these as sign to stay awake and alert, light from screens is not good either.
- Try to avoid exercising or eating too close to your bed time.
- Try to only use your bed for sleeping so your brain associates it with sleep. Avoid using devices in bed.
- Make sure you get lots of sunlight in the mornings and throughout the day. This can help with your natural rhythm and help you sleep at night.
- Make it regular. Your body responds well to waking and going to bed at the same times each day. This can ensure you get the most out of your sleep.

WARNING:

Although sleep is really important, try not to place too much effort on "trying" to get to sleep. You will have some days where it's harder to sleep than others. What's important is that you do your best during the day and before bed so you can allow sleep to come. If you get forceful or demanding with trying to get to sleep, it won't happen easily. If you're struggling to sleep, get up, find something to do, and then try to go back to bed again when you feel sleepy.

"At a very young age I learned how important sleep was. I really can't say it enough. I don't think people really pay enough attention to how important sleep is."
– Michael Phelps, 23-time Olympic Gold Medallist

THE MENTAL TOUGHNESS CHALLENGE

Deciding what you want to do and then doing it, regardless of how you feel in the moment, is a great away to continue to be mentally tough. Let's practise it. I challenge you!

If you can build one healthy habit into your day, I guarantee you will feel better about yourself and more confident in your ability to stick at things and keep progressing and growing. So let's do it! Let's choose something a little bit hard, but good for us. And let's do it every day!

With your challenge mindset you can see this as the Mental Toughness Challenge.

Can you commit to bringing ONE NEW HABIT into your life for 30 days?

It might be something like..

- Brushing or flossing teeth morning and night
- Having a glass of water every morning before breakfast
- Doing some mind training before bed every night
- Doing something nice for someone else, every single day
- Doing some form of exercise every day.

The choice is yours
(it has to be something that is positive for growing yourself as a person, i.e. not eating McDonalds every day for a month!)

You're doing this to help you build **Mental Toughness.** If you fail and forget to do the task, you have to START AGAIN at day 1. The challenge is to do it for **30 days**, then you can look back and see how well you've done! If you're ready to test yourself, then sign up right now and make the promise to yourself.

COMMIT TO THE CHALLENGE.

I commit to building my mental toughness by doing:

____

every day for 30 days.

Signed: ______________________ Date: ____________

TRACK YOUR PROGRESS (CROSS OFF EACH DAY WHEN YOU COMPLETE IT):

1 2 3 4 5 6 7 8 9 10 11 12 13 14 15 16 17 18 19 20 21 22 23 24 25 26 27 28 29 30

STAYING PRESENT

Like how a river flows, when we perform at our best, everything just flows! We let our body express itself through our performance. We completely focus on what we are doing. So how can we get better at this? **By practising to focus completely on a task!**

The following activities are about getting into the present moment, so you can leave the future and past behind you and perform at your best without being caught up by unhelpful thoughts.

If you do these things on a regular basis, and treat it like your physical training exercises, you will get better and better and see real benefit in your ability to maintain attention and concentrate on what you need to.

A COMMON COMPLAINT I HEAR IS THAT PEOPLE ARE TOO BUSY TO ENGAGE IN PRACTISING MIND TRAINING.

In actual fact, there are moments in everyday life that are perfect to practise staying present. It's great to practise in moments where our mind wanders – times when we do activities without actually thinking about what we're actually doing in that moment.

ANCHOR BREATHING

In this exercise you are using your breath as an anchor to the present moment. Being in the present moment is when you perform your best. You are able to focus completely and be absorbed by the task at hand.

The reason we are doing this is because your breathing is a great way to anchor yourself back to the present moment and let go of any unhelpful thoughts.

Letting go of unhelpful thoughts does not mean they go away. Our minds don't have an erase button, but we can choose to let them be there and focus our attention on what is important. The most important thing is what you are doing right now. For example, if you were a gymnast getting ready to perform a floor routine, you wouldn't want to be thinking about a poor (or good) performance that happened in the past or what might happen if you make a mistake in the future.

Make sure you are sitting comfortably. We are going to gently notice and observe our breathing for 5 minutes.

→

The goal is to focus on your breathing and the feelings that you get when you fill your lungs and slowly empty them.

↓

You might notice some things like the air from your nose passing over your upper lip, the feeling of filling your lungs, and the sounds of air whistling in and out.

←

Take note of everything and just be aware. If you notice your mind rushing toward the past or future, that is great! You're getting it!

↓

Then just gently bring it back to the breathing. Place your attention on your breathing. Be curious about it. This is the training part. You are connecting to your breath, which is the anchor to the present moment.

IF YOU GET BETTER AT THIS, YOU CAN TAKE A BREATH DURING COMPETITION AND RESET YOUR MIND, GETTING BACK TO THE NOW MORE EASILY! BUT YOU NEED TO PRACTISE.

So keep noticing how your mind starts wandering – how it thinks about all sorts of stuff, all the time. When you notice it thinking, say to yourself:

...and then focus attention on the breathing again.

OVER TIME, IF YOU PRACTISE THIS, YOU WILL GET BETTER AT LETTING GO OF NEGATIVE THINKING OR THOUGHTS THAT AREN'T HELPFUL.

Have a think about how you can build this into your life so it becomes regular practice.

SCHEDULE TIME TO PRACTICE THIS!

CENTRING EXERCISE

This exercise comes from martial arts, and is a great way to reset and "be where your feet are." This means bringing your attention back to where you are and away from the past or future. This also involves having good posture and strong body language. With your head up, shoulders back, and feet nice and balanced apart.

1. Stand with feet shoulder-width apart, with a soft/slight bend in the knees. Feel strong and balanced.

→

2. Take a deep breath in through the nose.

↓

3. On the exhale, you want to drag this out as long as you can. When you exhale, sink down into your feet spreading your weight evenly, feeling balanced and centred. Draw strength from the ground as you notice your connection to it.

←

4. Notice where you are, everything around you. Bring your attention to this place.

↓

5. Now re-focus on a task or cue that's important to you. You might reiterate a key word or value to remind you of what's important!

NOTICING 5 THINGS

This exercise is about anchoring yourself to the place you are, right now, by paying attention to it. We take our minds off our own thoughts and feelings and start by paying more attention to what is happening around us. Follow the instructions below:

1. Close your eyes (you can be sitting or standing). Focus on the sounds around you. See if you can notice 5 different sounds. Start with the loudest ones and then listen closer to any softer more distant sounds that are further away and harder to notice. Close your eyes and do this for 30 seconds.

2. Next, with your eyes still closed, notice what you can feel with your sense of touch. What can you feel on your skin? See if you can pay attention to this and notice as much as possible. Sit and know you are sitting. Feel the chair underneath you. The clothes on your skin, the breeze in your face. Try to find 5 things you can feel! Close your eyes and do this for around 30 seconds.

3. Now, gently open your eyes, pay attention to everything you can see around you. Look at it like you have never seen things before. Be very curious about all the things you are looking at. Notice them, and move on to noticing other things.

4. Lastly, the challenging part! Now you've engaged each sense by itself, you are going to practise doing this all at once. Just sit and notice all the things you can see, feel and hear. Turn your brain into the best paying attention machine.

BY DOING THE EXERCISE ABOVE ON A REGULAR BASIS, YOU WILL BECOME BETTER AT ANCHORING YOURSELF TO THE PRESENT MOMENT AND TAKING YOUR FOCUS OUT OF YOUR OWN THOUGHTS AND FEELINGS AND INTO THE OUTSIDE WORLD. THIS IS WHERE WE NEED TO BE MORE OFTEN, BECAUSE THAT'S WHERE WE PLAY OUR SPORT. BEING INSIDE OUR OWN HEADS (WITH OUR WORRIES, FEARS AND DOUBTS) IS GOING TO MEAN WE ARE UNABLE TO TRULY BE OURSELVES AND PERFORM AT OUR BEST.

OTHER WAYS TO GET PRESENT

AWARENESS WHEN LINING UP IN QUEUE

When you're waiting in a queue, resist the temptation to take out your phone and distract yourself to avoid the boredom.

Instead, take time to notice everything around you and what your mind is thinking and feeling. It might be harder, but it's great practice at not avoiding a feeling by taking your mind off the moment.

BRUSHING YOUR TEETH

Ever stopped to think about what you are thinking about when you are brushing your teeth? Try it! You will be amazed at how automatic the process usually is.

Take time to pay attention to everything about the brushing of your teeth. The feel of the bristles, the movement of your arm, the grip of your fingers etc. Engage with the process and notice what thoughts come up and interrupt you.

MINDFUL TRAVELLING

If you sit in a car, bus, train, tram, car, subway or helicopter on your way to school or work, then use this time to sit and take notice of your thoughts and feelings and take in the world around you.

WOW

Resist the temptation to avoid the "boredom" by using your phone or reading, and just sit and be. Notice the thoughts that want to pull you away, and refocus on this moment.

SHOWER OR BATH

When we take a shower or bath we are often spending the whole time thinking about something else and not what we are actually doing.

This is OK, but you could treat it as an opportunity to really focus on the experience and notice everything about what you are doing!

GOOD

Try planning to eat some meals more slowly and mindfully so you pay attention to every part of the meal – what the food feels and tastes like as you chew and swallow your food. Notice each thing that's interesting about your food.

EATING

I don't know about you, but sometimes I finish a meal and wonder where the food went and whether or not it even tasted good! Sometimes I am too busy away with my thoughts (or in a conversation) to pay attention to what the food felt like, smelt like, and tasted like.

SURFING THROUGH YOUR FEELINGS

You may or may not have been near the ocean, but hopefully you know what an ocean wave is like. They are amazing things. They travel hundreds of miles as swell, then when they get close to shore they rise up high, collapse and wash up on the beach, and disappear. Our emotions are a lot like this – if we avoid struggling with them.

One way to handle some of the tough times in sport and in life in general is to treat it like you're riding a wave. It will build up, reach its peak, and then fade away. It won't last forever. So, follow the steps below to ride your emotions like you're riding a wave. SURF'S UP!

OBSERVE HOW YOU ARE FEELING AND HOW YOUR BODY IS REACTING TO THAT. LABEL THE FEELINGS AND SENSATIONS IN YOUR BODY. SAY TO YOURSELF, "I AM NOTICING (WHATEVER YOU ARE FEELING)."

→

NOTICE ALSO WHAT YOU ARE THINKING AND WORRYING ABOUT. ACKNOWLEDGE THEM WITHOUT TRYING TO CHANGE THEM.

↓

NOW FEEL WHERE THE "WAVE" OF FEELINGS ARE AT. JUST NOTICE. ARE THEY INCREASING, OR DO THEY FEEL LIKE THEY ARE AT THE PEAK? ACCEPT WHEREVER THEY ARE. LET IT BE. BREATHE INTO THE FEELINGS THAT ARE THERE.

←

THE WAVE MOVES AT ITS OWN SPEED. TRY TO WATCH AND FEEL IT ALL WITH ACCEPTANCE, LIKE YOU'RE GOING FOR THE RIDE RATHER THAN FORCING OR FIGHTING ANYTHING. YOU DON'T HAVE TO FIGHT THE WAVES. LEARN TO RIDE THEM INSTEAD!

REMEMBER: YOU CAN'T ALWAYS CHOOSE HOW YOU FEEL, BUT YOU CAN CHOOSE WHAT YOU FOCUS ON.

YOU CAN CHOOSE HOW YOU RESPOND.

BOX BREATHING

Box breathing is a way of controlling your breathing. If you are feeling overwhelmed, unfocused, anxious or stressed, try box breathing. It helps you inhale and exhale at the same rate (4 seconds) and it can help give you a sense of control and calmness to your body and your brain. It can help you focus under pressure. Give it a go!

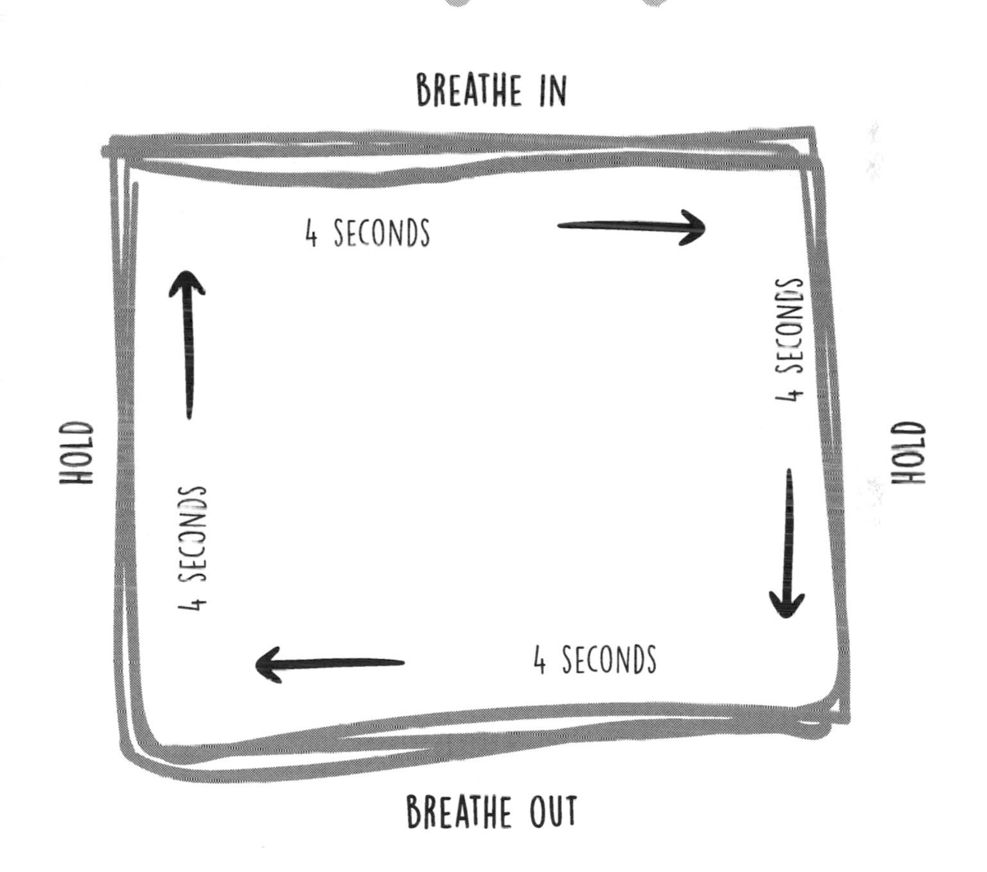

NOTES PAGE

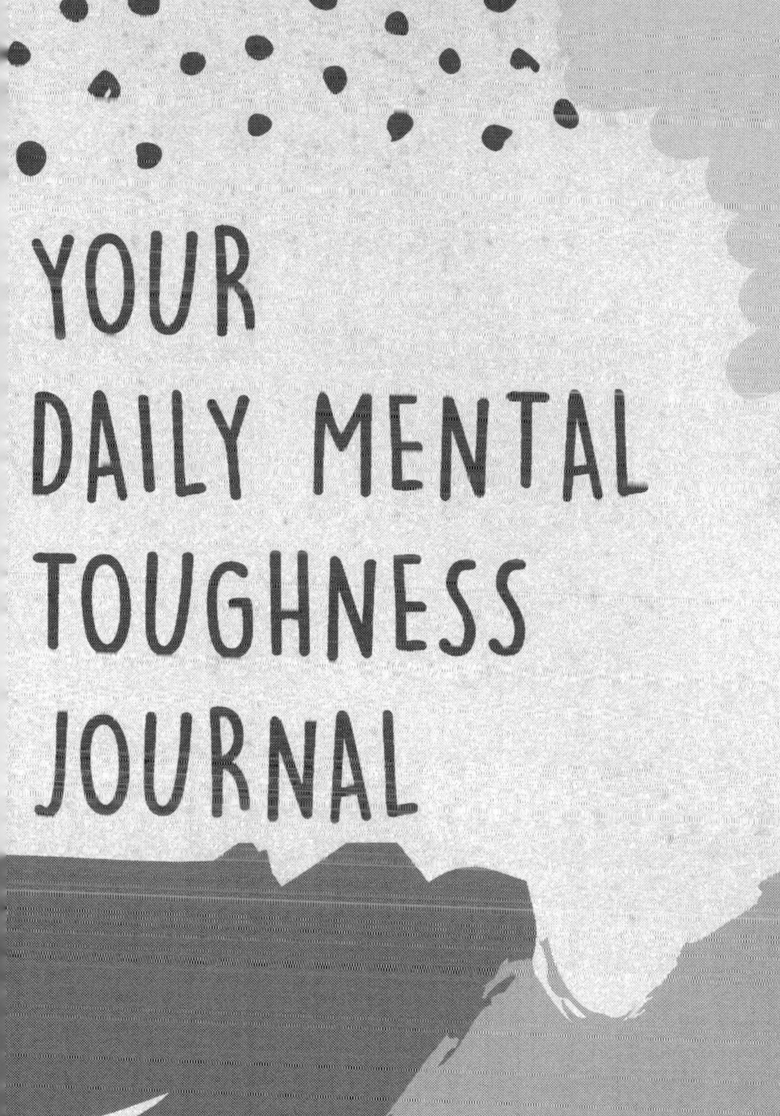
YOUR
DAILY MENTAL
TOUGHNESS
JOURNAL

HOW TO USE THE DAILY JOURNAL

The following Journal pages are designed to help you prepare, plan, and then reflect on your day. When you make a good plan it can help you feel a lot more confident and optimistic. It always feels good to have a plan!

All that aside, this is the part where you go ahead and create a day that you will be proud of!

JUST REMEMBER: YOU CAN BE FLEXIBLE TOO. NOT EVERYTHING GOES TO PLAN, AND WE NEVER KNOW WHAT LIFE WILL THROW AT US.

YOUR STARTING POINT: it's nice to begin any day by thinking about what you can be thankful for. There's lots of evidence to show that if you begin your day thinking about the things you can be thankful for, then it can kickstart a good mood and make you feel a whole lot better. So go ahead and identify what you can be grateful for!

We build Mental Toughness by going towards things that scare us. They don't always have to be big things, but often there are worthwhile challenges that we can do each day that are hard. This is usually things that make us a little uncomfortable. Name some stuff that you might usually avoid and commit to doing it!

NOW, WHAT'S WRITTEN IN THE BOX AT THE TOP IS ALSO REALLY IMPORTANT. YOUR COURAGEOUS STUFF TO DO TODAY.

WRITE THEM IN AT THE TOP OF THE JOURNAL AND THEN DECIDE WHEN YOU WILL GET IT DONE.

Next are the spaces for your values. I find it is helpful to focus on no more than three for the day. You might be doing something that will require a quality that you want to bring out on that day. For example, you could be running a race and you might want to focus on Perseverance or Giving it everything you've got.

THE REAL KEY TO THESE VALUES IS THAT THEY ARE IMPORTANT BECAUSE THEY ARE ALWAYS POSSIBLE!

WE CAN CHOOSE TO BE THE PERSON WE WANT TO BE IN EVERY SITUATION! SO GO FOR IT!

BELOW THAT, YOU HAVE SOME SPACE TO WRITE DOWN SOME PLANS OR THINGS TO FOCUS ON FOR THE DAY, THE PRACTICE, OR THE COMPETITION.

It's up to you how you use it! This could include goals, targets, or just things you need to remember to do.Plan out what you want to achieve at the training or just the whole day in general. This journal is flexible, so you can decide how you use this planning page.

HOW TO USE THE REFLECTION PAGE

This is where the magic happens!

Scientists have proven that learning is super-charged if we spend some time to reflect back, go over and talk about what happened. Then the next step is to think about what you could do better and what actions you are going to take as a result of that. That helps keep you moving in the right direction.

THIS COULD BE THE PAGE THAT BENEFITS YOU THE MOST!

IT'S UP TO YOU HOW YOU USE THIS. YOU COULD DO YOUR REFLECTION AT THE END OF A DAY, OR JUST AFTER A PRACTICE OR A COMPETITION.

IF YOU FEEL COMFORTABLE DOING SO, YOU CAN ALSO TALK WITH A COACH, TEACHER OR PARENT AND GO THROUGH THIS SECTION TOGETHER!

DATE:

What things can I be grateful for today?

How will I be courageous today?

What values can I focus on today?

JOURNAL

Below is your space to write your schedule, the goals to focus on today, mental training to do, plans for the future, struggles you're going through or how you're feeling. You can write anything you want!

REFLECTIONS

What went well?

What did I learn today?

What actions will I take now, based on what I have learnt?

RATINGS FOR TODAY

Give yourself a score from 0-10 on the scales below on how well you did in these areas:

VALUES

0 10

How well did I live as "the person I wanted to be?"

EFFORT

0 10

How hard did I try?

COURAGE

0 10

How brave was I?

DATE: ______________________

What things can I be grateful for today?

How will I be courageous today?

What values can I focus on today?

JOURNAL

Below is your space to write your schedule, the goals to focus on today, mental training to do, plans for the future, struggles you're going through or how you're feeling. You can write anything you want!

REFLECTIONS

What went well?

What did I learn today?

What actions will I take now, based on what I have learnt?

RATINGS FOR TODAY

Give yourself a score from 0-10 on the scales below on how well you did in these areas:

VALUES

0 10

How well did I live as "the person I wanted to be?"

EFFORT

0 10

How hard did I try?

COURAGE

0 10

How brave was I?

DATE:

What things can I be grateful for today?

How will I be courageous today?

What values can I focus on today?

JOURNAL

Below is your space to write your schedule, the goals to focus on today, mental training to do, plans for the future, struggles you're going through or how you're feeling. You can write anything you want!

REFLECTIONS

What went well?

What did I learn today?

What actions will I take now, based on what I have learnt?

RATINGS FOR TODAY

Give yourself a score from 0-10 on the scales below on how well you did in these areas:

VALUES

0 — 10

How well did I live as "the person I wanted to be?"

EFFORT

0 — 10

How hard did I try?

COURAGE

0 — 10

How brave was I?

DATE:

What things can I be grateful for today?

How will I be courageous today?

What values can I focus on today?

JOURNAL

Below is your space to write your schedule, the goals to focus on today, mental training to do, plans for the future, struggles you're going through or how you're feeling. You can write anything you want!

REFLECTIONS

What went well?

What did I learn today?

What actions will I take now, based on what I have learnt?

RATINGS FOR TODAY

Give yourself a score from 0-10 on the scales below on how well you did in these areas:

VALUES

0 — 10

How well did I live as "the person I wanted to be?"

EFFORT

0 — 10

How hard did I try?

COURAGE

0 — 10

How brave was I?

DATE:

What things can I be grateful for today?

How will I be courageous today?

What values can I focus on today?

JOURNAL

Below is your space to write your schedule, the goals to focus on today, mental training to do, plans for the future, struggles you're going through or how you're feeling. You can write anything you want!

REFLECTIONS

What went well?

What did I learn today?

What actions will I take now, based on what I have learnt?

RATINGS FOR TODAY

Give yourself a score from 0-10 on the scales below on how well you did in these areas:

VALUES

0 10

How well did I live as "the person I wanted to be?"

EFFORT

0 10

How hard did I try?

COURAGE

0 10

How brave was I?

"If there is no struggle,
there is no progress."

- Frederick Douglass

HOW ARE THINGS GOING FOR YOU?

REFLECT ON WHAT YOU'VE ACHIEVED AND WHAT YOU'RE PROUD OF:

DATE: ______________________

What things can I be grateful for today?

How will I be courageous today?

What values can I focus on today?

JOURNAL

Below is your space to write your schedule, the goals to focus on today, mental training to do, plans for the future, struggles you're going through or how you're feeling. You can write anything you want!

REFLECTIONS

What went well?

What did I learn today?

What actions will I take now, based on what I have learnt?

RATINGS FOR TODAY

Give yourself a score from 0-10 on the scales below on how well you did in these areas:

VALUES

0 10

How well did I live as "the person I wanted to be?"

EFFORT

0 10

How hard did I try?

COURAGE

0 10

How brave was I?

DATE:______________________

What things can I be grateful for today?

How will I be courageous today?

What values can I focus on today?

JOURNAL

Below is your space to write your schedule, the goals to focus on today, mental training to do, plans for the future, struggles you're going through or how you're feeling. You can write anything you want!

REFLECTIONS

What went well?

What did I learn today?

What actions will I take now, based on what I have learnt?

RATINGS FOR TODAY

Give yourself a score from 0-10 on the scales below on how well you did in these areas:

VALUES

0 10

How well did I live as "the person I wanted to be?"

EFFORT

0 10

How hard did I try?

COURAGE

0 10

How brave was I?

DATE: ______________________

What things can I be grateful for today?

How will I be courageous today?

What values can I focus on today?

JOURNAL

Below is your space to write your schedule, the goals to focus on today, mental training to do, plans for the future, struggles you're going through or how you're feeling. You can write anything you want!

REFLECTIONS

What went well?

What did I learn today?

What actions will I take now, based on what I have learnt?

RATINGS FOR TODAY

Give yourself a score from 0-10 on the scales below on how well you did in these areas:

VALUES

0 10

How well did I live as "the person I wanted to be?"

EFFORT

0 10

How hard did I try?

COURAGE

0 10

How brave was I?

DATE:

What things can I be grateful for today?

How will I be courageous today?

What values can I focus on today?

JOURNAL

Below is your space to write your schedule, the goals to focus on today, mental training to do, plans for the future, struggles you're going through or how you're feeling. You can write anything you want!

REFLECTIONS

What went well?

What did I learn today?

What actions will I take now, based on what I have learnt?

RATINGS FOR TODAY

Give yourself a score from 0-10 on the scales below on how well you did in these areas:

VALUES

0 10

How well did I live as "the person I wanted to be?"

EFFORT

0 10

How hard did I try?

COURAGE

0 10

How brave was I?

DATE: ______________________

What things can I be grateful for today?

How will I be courageous today?

What values can I focus on today?

JOURNAL

Below is your space to write your schedule, the goals to focus on today, mental training to do, plans for the future, struggles you're going through or how you're feeling. You can write anything you want!

REFLECTIONS

What went well?

What did I learn today?

What actions will I take now, based on what I have learnt?

RATINGS FOR TODAY

Give yourself a score from 0-10 on the scales below on how well you did in these areas:

VALUES

0 10

How well did I live as "the person I wanted to be?"

EFFORT

0 10

How hard did I try?

COURAGE

0 10

How brave was I?

"A champion is someone who gets up when he can't"
- Jack Dempsey

HOW ARE THINGS GOING FOR YOU?

REFLECT ON WHAT YOU'VE ACHIEVED AND WHAT YOU'RE PROUD OF:

DATE: ______________________

What things can I be grateful for today?

How will I be courageous today?

What values can I focus on today?

JOURNAL

Below is your space to write your schedule, the goals to focus on today, mental training to do, plans for the future, struggles you're going through or how you're feeling. You can write anything you want!

REFLECTIONS

What went well?

What did I learn today?

What actions will I take now, based on what I have learnt?

RATINGS FOR TODAY

Give yourself a score from 0-10 on the scales below on how well you did in these areas:

VALUES

0 10

How well did I live as "the person I wanted to be?"

EFFORT

0 10

How hard did I try?

COURAGE

0 10

How brave was I?

DATE:

What things can I be grateful for today?

How will I be courageous today?

What values can I focus on today?

JOURNAL

Below is your space to write your schedule, the goals to focus on today, mental training to do, plans for the future, struggles you're going through or how you're feeling. You can write anything you want!

REFLECTIONS

What went well?

What did I learn today?

What actions will I take now, based on what I have learnt?

RATINGS FOR TODAY

Give yourself a score from 0-10 on the scales below on how well you did in these areas:

VALUES

0 10

How well did I live as "the person I wanted to be?"

EFFORT

0 10

How hard did I try?

COURAGE

0 10

How brave was I?

DATE:

What things can I be grateful for today?

How will I be courageous today?

What values can I focus on today?

JOURNAL

Below is your space to write your schedule, the goals to focus on today, mental training to do, plans for the future, struggles you're going through or how you're feeling. You can write anything you want!

REFLECTIONS

What went well?

What did I learn today?

What actions will I take now, based on what I have learnt?

RATINGS FOR TODAY

Give yourself a score from 0-10 on the scales below on how well you did in these areas:

VALUES

0 10

How well did I live as "the person I wanted to be?"

EFFORT

0 10

How hard did I try?

COURAGE

0 10

How brave was I?

DATE: ______

What things can I be grateful for today?

How will I be courageous today?

What values can I focus on today?

JOURNAL

Below is your space to write your schedule, the goals to focus on today, mental training to do, plans for the future, struggles you're going through or how you're feeling. You can write anything you want!

REFLECTIONS

What went well?

What did I learn today?

What actions will I take now, based on what I have learnt?

RATINGS FOR TODAY

Give yourself a score from 0-10 on the scales below on how well you did in these areas:

VALUES

0 10

How well did I live as "the person I wanted to be?"

EFFORT

0 10

How hard did I try?

COURAGE

0 10

How brave was I?

DATE: ____________________

What things can I be grateful for today?

How will I be courageous today?

What values can I focus on today?

JOURNAL

Below is your space to write your schedule, the goals to focus on today, mental training to do, plans for the future, struggles you're going through or how you're feeling. You can write anything you want!

REFLECTIONS

What went well?

What did I learn today?

What actions will I take now, based on what I have learnt?

RATINGS FOR TODAY

Give yourself a score from 0-10 on the scales below on how well you did in these areas:

VALUES

0 10

How well did I live as "the person I wanted to be?"

EFFORT

0 10

How hard did I try?

COURAGE

0 10

How brave was I?

"You miss 100% of the shots you don't take"

- Wayne Gretsky

HOW ARE THINGS GOING FOR YOU?

REFLECT ON WHAT YOU'VE ACHIEVED AND WHAT YOU'RE PROUD OF:

DATE: ______________________

What things can I be grateful for today?

How will I be courageous today?

What values can I focus on today?

JOURNAL

Below is your space to write your schedule, the goals to focus on today, mental training to do, plans for the future, struggles you're going through or how you're feeling. You can write anything you want!

REFLECTIONS

What went well?

What did I learn today?

What actions will I take now, based on what I have learnt?

RATINGS FOR TODAY

Give yourself a score from 0-10 on the scales below on how well you did in these areas:

VALUES

0 — 10

How well did I live as "the person I wanted to be?"

EFFORT

0 — 10

How hard did I try?

COURAGE

0 — 10

How brave was I?

DATE:

What things can I be grateful for today?

How will I be courageous today?

What values can I focus on today?

JOURNAL

Below is your space to write your schedule, the goals to focus on today, mental training to do, plans for the future, struggles you're going through or how you're feeling. You can write anything you want!

REFLECTIONS

What went well?

What did I learn today?

What actions will I take now, based on what I have learnt?

RATINGS FOR TODAY

Give yourself a score from 0-10 on the scales below on how well you did in these areas:

VALUES

0 — 10

How well did I live as "the person I wanted to be?"

EFFORT

0 — 10

How hard did I try?

COURAGE

0 — 10

How brave was I?

DATE: ______________________________

What things can I be grateful for today?

How will I be courageous today?

What values can I focus on today?

JOURNAL

Below is your space to write your schedule, the goals to focus on today, mental training to do, plans for the future, struggles you're going through or how you're feeling. You can write anything you want!

REFLECTIONS

What went well?

What did I learn today?

What actions will I take now, based on what I have learnt?

RATINGS FOR TODAY

Give yourself a score from 0-10 on the scales below on how well you did in these areas:

VALUES

0 10

How well did I live as "the person I wanted to be?"

EFFORT

0 10

How hard did I try?

COURAGE

0 10

How brave was I?

DATE:

What things can I be grateful for today?

How will I be courageous today?

What values can I focus on today?

JOURNAL

Below is your space to write your schedule, the goals to focus on today, mental training to do, plans for the future, struggles you're going through or how you're feeling. You can write anything you want!

REFLECTIONS

What went well?

What did I learn today?

What actions will I take now, based on what I have learnt?

RATINGS FOR TODAY

Give yourself a score from 0-10 on the scales below on how well you did in these areas:

VALUES

0 10

How well did I live as "the person I wanted to be?"

EFFORT

0 10

How hard did I try?

COURAGE

0 10

How brave was I?

DATE: ______________________

What things can I be grateful for today?

How will I be courageous today?

What values can I focus on today?

JOURNAL

Below is your space to write your schedule, the goals to focus on today, mental training to do, plans for the future, struggles you're going through or how you're feeling. You can write anything you want!

REFLECTIONS

What went well?

What did I learn today?

What actions will I take now, based on what I have learnt?

RATINGS FOR TODAY

Give yourself a score from 0-10 on the scales below on how well you did in these areas:

VALUES

0 10

How well did I live as "the person I wanted to be?"

EFFORT

0 10

How hard did I try?

COURAGE

0 10

How brave was I?

"Don't ask yourself what the world needs, ask yourself what makes you come alive and then do that. Because what the world needs is more people who have come alive."

- Howard Thurman

HOW ARE THINGS GOING FOR YOU?

REFLECT ON WHAT YOU'VE ACHIEVED AND WHAT YOU'RE PROUD OF:

DATE: ______________________

What things can I be grateful for today?

How will I be courageous today?

What values can I focus on today?

JOURNAL

Below is your space to write your schedule, the goals to focus on today, mental training to do, plans for the future, struggles you're going through or how you're feeling. You can write anything you want!

REFLECTIONS

What went well?

What did I learn today?

What actions will I take now, based on what I have learnt?

RATINGS FOR TODAY

Give yourself a score from 0-10 on the scales below on how well you did in these areas:

VALUES

0 10

How well did I live as "the person I wanted to be?"

EFFORT

0 10

How hard did I try?

COURAGE

0 10

How brave was I?

DATE: ____________________

What things can I be grateful for today?

How will I be courageous today?

What values can I focus on today?

JOURNAL

Below is your space to write your schedule, the goals to focus on today, mental training to do, plans for the future, struggles you're going through or how you're feeling. You can write anything you want!

REFLECTIONS

What went well?

What did I learn today?

What actions will I take now, based on what I have learnt?

RATINGS FOR TODAY

Give yourself a score from 0-10 on the scales below on how well you did in these areas:

VALUES

0 — 10

How well did I live as "the person I wanted to be?"

EFFORT

0 — 10

How hard did I try?

COURAGE

0 — 10

How brave was I?

DATE: ______________________

What things can I be grateful for today?

How will I be courageous today?

What values can I focus on today?

JOURNAL

Below is your space to write your schedule, the goals to focus on today, mental training to do, plans for the future, struggles you're going through or how you're feeling. You can write anything you want!

REFLECTIONS

What went well?

What did I learn today?

What actions will I take now, based on what I have learnt?

RATINGS FOR TODAY

Give yourself a score from 0-10 on the scales below on how well you did in these areas:

VALUES

0 10

How well did I live as "the person I wanted to be?"

EFFORT

0 10

How hard did I try?

COURAGE

0 10

How brave was I?

DATE:

What things can I be grateful for today?

How will I be courageous today?

What values can I focus on today?

JOURNAL

Below is your space to write your schedule, the goals to focus on today, mental training to do, plans for the future, struggles you're going through or how you're feeling. You can write anything you want!

REFLECTIONS

What went well?

What did I learn today?

What actions will I take now, based on what I have learnt?

RATINGS FOR TODAY

Give yourself a score from 0-10 on the scales below on how well you did in these areas:

VALUES

0 10

How well did I live as "the person I wanted to be?"

EFFORT

0 10

How hard did I try?

COURAGE

0 10

How brave was I?

DATE:

What things can I be grateful for today?

How will I be courageous today?

What Values can I focus on today?

JOURNAL

Below is your space to write your schedule, the goals to focus on today, mental training to do, plans for the future, struggles you're going through or how you're feeling. You can write anything you want!

REFLECTIONS

What went well?

What did I learn today?

What actions will I take now, based on what I have learnt?

RATINGS FOR TODAY

Give yourself a score from 0-10 on the scales below on how well you did in these areas:

VALUES

0 — 10

How well did I live as "the person I wanted to be?"

EFFORT

0 — 10

How hard did I try?

COURAGE

0 — 10

How brave was I?

"The greatest glory lies not
in never falling, but in rising
every time we fall."

- Nelson Mandela

HOW ARE THINGS GOING FOR YOU?

REFLECT ON WHAT YOU'VE ACHIEVED AND WHAT YOU'RE PROUD OF:

DATE:

What things can I be grateful for today?

How will I be courageous today?

What values can I focus on today?

JOURNAL

Below is your space to write your schedule, the goals to focus on today, mental training to do, plans for the future, struggles you're going through or how you're feeling. You can write anything you want!

REFLECTIONS

What went well?

What did I learn today?

What actions will I take now, based on what I have learnt?

RATINGS FOR TODAY

Give yourself a score from 0-10 on the scales below on how well you did in these areas:

VALUES

0 10

How well did I live as "the person I wanted to be?"

EFFORT

0 10

How hard did I try?

COURAGE

0 10

How brave was I?

DATE: ____________________

What things can I be grateful for today?

How will I be courageous today?

What values can I focus on today?

JOURNAL

Below is your space to write your schedule, the goals to focus on today, mental training to do, plans for the future, struggles you're going through or how you're feeling. You can write anything you want!

REFLECTIONS

What went well?

What did I learn today?

What actions will I take now, based on what I have learnt?

RATINGS FOR TODAY

Give yourself a score from 0-10 on the scales below on how well you did in these areas:

VALUES

0 10

How well did I live as "the person I wanted to be?"

EFFORT

0 10

How hard did I try?

COURAGE

0 10

How brave was I?

DATE: ______________________

What things can I be grateful for today?

How will I be courageous today?

What values can I focus on today?

JOURNAL

Below is your space to write your schedule, the goals to focus on today, mental training to do, plans for the future, struggles you're going through or how you're feeling. You can write anything you want!

REFLECTIONS

What went well?

What did I learn today?

What actions will I take now, based on what I have learnt?

RATINGS FOR TODAY

Give yourself a score from 0-10 on the scales below on how well you did in these areas:

VALUES

0 10

How well did I live as "the person I wanted to be?"

EFFORT

0 10

How hard did I try?

COURAGE

0 10

How brave was I?

DATE: ____________________

What things can I be grateful for today?

How will I be courageous today?

What values can I focus on today?

JOURNAL

Below is your space to write your schedule, the goals to focus on today, mental training to do, plans for the future, struggles you're going through or how you're feeling. You can write anything you want!

REFLECTIONS

What went well?

What did I learn today?

What actions will I take now, based on what I have learnt?

RATINGS FOR TODAY

Give yourself a score from 0-10 on the scales below on how well you did in these areas:

VALUES

0 10

How well did I live as "the person I wanted to be?"

EFFORT

0 10

How hard did I try?

COURAGE

0 10

How brave was I?

DATE: ____________________

What things can I be grateful for today?

How will I be courageous today?

What values can I focus on today?

JOURNAL

Below is your space to write your schedule, the goals to focus on today, mental training to do, plans for the future, struggles you're going through or how you're feeling. You can write anything you want!

REFLECTIONS

What went well?

What did I learn today?

What actions will I take now, based on what I have learnt?

RATINGS FOR TODAY

Give yourself a score from 0-10 on the scales below on how well you did in these areas:

VALUES

0 — 10

How well did I live as "the person I wanted to be?"

EFFORT

0 — 10

How hard did I try?

COURAGE

0 — 10

How brave was I?

"Our one true home is
in the present moment."
- Thich Nhat Hanh

HOW ARE THINGS GOING FOR YOU?

REFLECT ON WHAT YOU'VE ACHIEVED AND WHAT YOU'RE PROUD OF:

DATE:

What things can I be grateful for today?

How will I be courageous today?

What values can I focus on today?

JOURNAL

Below is your space to write your schedule, the goals to focus on today, mental training to do, plans for the future, struggles you're going through or how you're feeling. You can write anything you want!

REFLECTIONS

What went well?

What did I learn today?

What actions will I take now, based on what I have learnt?

RATINGS FOR TODAY

Give yourself a score from 0-10 on the scales below on how well you did in these areas:

VALUES

0 10

How well did I live as "the person I wanted to be?"

EFFORT

0 10

How hard did I try?

COURAGE

0 10

How brave was I?

DATE: ____________________

What things can I be grateful for today?

How will I be courageous today?

What values can I focus on today?

JOURNAL

Below is your space to write your schedule, the goals to focus on today, mental training to do, plans for the future, struggles you're going through or how you're feeling. You can write anything you want!

REFLECTIONS

What went well?

What did I learn today?

What actions will I take now, based on what I have learnt?

RATINGS FOR TODAY

Give yourself a score from 0-10 on the scales below on how well you did in these areas:

VALUES

0 — 10

How well did I live as "the person I wanted to be?"

EFFORT

0 — 10

How hard did I try?

COURAGE

0 — 10

How brave was I?

DATE:

What things can I be grateful for today?

How will I be courageous today?

What values can I focus on today?

JOURNAL

Below is your space to write your schedule, the goals to focus on today, mental training to do, plans for the future, struggles you're going through or how you're feeling. You can write anything you want!

REFLECTIONS

What went well?

What did I learn today?

What actions will I take now, based on what I have learnt?

RATINGS FOR TODAY

Give yourself a score from 0-10 on the scales below on how well you did in these areas:

VALUES

0 10

How well did I live as "the person I wanted to be?"

EFFORT

0 10

How hard did I try?

COURAGE

0 10

How brave was I?

DATE:

What things can I be grateful for today?

How will I be courageous today?

What values can I focus on today?

JOURNAL

Below is your space to write your schedule, the goals to focus on today, mental training to do, plans for the future, struggles you're going through or how you're feeling. You can write anything you want!

REFLECTIONS

What went well?

What did I learn today?

What actions will I take now, based on what I have learnt?

RATINGS FOR TODAY

Give yourself a score from 0-10 on the scales below on how well you did in these areas:

VALUES

0 10

How well did I live as "the person I wanted to be?"

EFFORT

0 10

How hard did I try?

COURAGE

0 10

How brave was I?

DATE:

What things can I be grateful for today?

How will I be courageous today?

What values can I focus on today?

JOURNAL

Below is your space to write your schedule, the goals to focus on today, mental training to do, plans for the future, struggles you're going through or how you're feeling. You can write anything you want!

REFLECTIONS

What went well?

What did I learn today?

What actions will I take now, based on what I have learnt?

RATINGS FOR TODAY

Give yourself a score from 0-10 on the scales below on how well you did in these areas:

VALUES

0 — 10

How well did I live as "the person I wanted to be?"

EFFORT

0 — 10

How hard did I try?

COURAGE

0 — 10

How brave was I?

"When a great ship is in harbour and moored, it is safe, there can be no doubt. But that is not what great ships are built for."

- Clarissa Pinkola Estes

HOW ARE THINGS GOING FOR YOU?

REFLECT ON WHAT YOU'VE ACHIEVED AND WHAT YOU'RE PROUD OF:

DATE: ____________________

What things can I be grateful for today?

How will I be courageous today?

What values can I focus on today?

JOURNAL

Below is your space to write your schedule, the goals to focus on today, mental training to do, plans for the future, struggles you're going through or how you're feeling. You can write anything you want!

REFLECTIONS

What went well?

What did I learn today?

What actions will I take now, based on what I have learnt?

RATINGS FOR TODAY

Give yourself a score from 0-10 on the scales below on how well you did in these areas:

VALUES

0 — 10

How well did I live as "the person I wanted to be?"

EFFORT

0 — 10

How hard did I try?

COURAGE

0 — 10

How brave was I?

DATE:

What things can I be grateful for today?

How will I be courageous today?

What values can I focus on today?

JOURNAL

Below is your space to write your schedule, the goals to focus on today, mental training to do, plans for the future, struggles you're going through or how you're feeling. You can write anything you want!

REFLECTIONS

What went well?

What did I learn today?

What actions will I take now, based on what I have learnt?

RATINGS FOR TODAY

Give yourself a score from 0-10 on the scales below on how well you did in these areas:

VALUES

0 10

How well did I live as "the person I wanted to be?"

EFFORT

0 10

How hard did I try?

COURAGE

0 10

How brave was I?

DATE:

What things can I be grateful for today?

How will I be courageous today?

What values can I focus on today?

JOURNAL

Below is your space to write your schedule, the goals to focus on today, mental training to do, plans for the future, struggles you're going through or how you're feeling. You can write anything you want!

REFLECTIONS

What went well?

What did I learn today?

What actions will I take now, based on what I have learnt?

RATINGS FOR TODAY

Give yourself a score from 0-10 on the scales below on how well you did in these areas:

VALUES

0 — 10

How well did I live as "the person I wanted to be?"

EFFORT

0 — 10

How hard did I try?

COURAGE

0 — 10

How brave was I?

DATE:

What things can I be grateful for today?

How will I be courageous today?

What values can I focus on today?

JOURNAL

Below is your space to write your schedule, the goals to focus on today, mental training to do, plans for the future, struggles you're going through or how you're feeling. You can write anything you want!

REFLECTIONS

What went well?

What did I learn today?

What actions will I take now, based on what I have learnt?

RATINGS FOR TODAY

Give yourself a score from 0-10 on the scales below on how well you did in these areas:

VALUES

0 10

How well did I live as "the person I wanted to be?"

EFFORT

0 10

How hard did I try?

COURAGE

0 10

How brave was I?

DATE: ____________________

What things can I be grateful for today?

How will I be courageous today?

What values can I focus on today?

JOURNAL

Below is your space to write your schedule, the goals to focus on today, mental training to do, plans for the future, struggles you're going through or how you're feeling. You can write anything you want!

REFLECTIONS

What went well?

What did I learn today?

What actions will I take now, based on what I have learnt?

RATINGS FOR TODAY

Give yourself a score from 0-10 on the scales below on how well you did in these areas:

VALUES

0 10

How well did I live as "the person I wanted to be?"

EFFORT

0 10

How hard did I try?

COURAGE

0 10

How brave was I?

"It is impossible to live without failing at something, unless you live so cautiously that you might as well not have lived at all - in which case, you fail by default."

- J.K. Rowling

HOW ARE THINGS GOING FOR YOU?

REFLECT ON WHAT YOU'VE ACHIEVED AND WHAT YOU'RE PROUD OF:

DATE:

What things can I be grateful for today?

How will I be courageous today?

What values can I focus on today?

JOURNAL

Below is your space to write your schedule, the goals to focus on today, mental training to do, plans for the future, struggles you're going through or how you're feeling. You can write anything you want!

REFLECTIONS

What went well?

What did I learn today?

What actions will I take now, based on what I have learnt?

RATINGS FOR TODAY

Give yourself a score from 0 10 on the scales below on how well you did in these areas:

VALUES

0 10

How well did I live as "the person I wanted to be?"

EFFORT

0 10

How hard did I try?

COURAGE

0 10

How brave was I?

DATE: ______

What things can I be grateful for today?

How will I be courageous today?

What values can I focus on today?

JOURNAL

Below is your space to write your schedule, the goals to focus on today, mental training to do, plans for the future, struggles you're going through or how you're feeling. You can write anything you want!

REFLECTIONS

What went well?

What did I learn today?

What actions will I take now, based on what I have learnt?

RATINGS FOR TODAY

Give yourself a score from 0-10 on the scales below on how well you did in these areas:

VALUES

0 10

How well did I live as "the person I wanted to be?"

EFFORT

0 10

How hard did I try?

COURAGE

0 10

How brave was I?

DATE:

What things can I be grateful for today?

How will I be courageous today?

What values can I focus on today?

JOURNAL

Below is your space to write your schedule, the goals to focus on today, mental training to do, plans for the future, struggles you're going through or how you're feeling. You can write anything you want!

REFLECTIONS

What went well?

What did I learn today?

What actions will I take now, based on what I have learnt?

RATINGS FOR TODAY

Give yourself a score from 0-10 on the scales below on how well you did in these areas:

VALUES

0 — 10

How well did I live as "the person I wanted to be?"

EFFORT

0 — 10

How hard did I try?

COURAGE

0 — 10

How brave was I?

DATE: ______________________

What things can I be grateful for today?

How will I be courageous today?

What values can I focus on today?

JOURNAL

Below is your space to write your schedule, the goals to focus on today, mental training to do, plans for the future, struggles you're going through or how you're feeling. You can write anything you want!

REFLECTIONS

What went well?

What did I learn today?

What actions will I take now, based on what I have learnt?

RATINGS FOR TODAY

Give yourself a score from 0-10 on the scales below on how well you did in these areas:

VALUES

0 10

How well did I live as "the person I wanted to be?"

EFFORT

0 10

How hard did I try?

COURAGE

0 10

How brave was I?

DATE:

What things can I be grateful for today?

How will I be courageous today?

What values can I focus on today?

JOURNAL

Below is your space to write your schedule, the goals to focus on today, mental training to do, plans for the future, struggles you're going through or how you're feeling. You can write anything you want!

REFLECTIONS

What went well?

What did I learn today?

What actions will I take now, based on what I have learnt?

RATINGS FOR TODAY

Give yourself a score from 0-10 on the scales below on how well you did in these areas:

VALUES

0 — 10

How well did I live as "the person I wanted to be?"

EFFORT

0 — 10

How hard did I try?

COURAGE

0 — 10

How brave was I?

"Gold medals aren't really made of gold. They're made of sweat, determination, and a hard-to-find alloy called guts."

- Dan Gable

HOW ARE THINGS GOING FOR YOU?

REFLECT ON WHAT YOU'VE ACHIEVED AND WHAT YOU'RE PROUD OF:

DATE:

What things can I be grateful for today?

How will I be courageous today?

What values can I focus on today?

JOURNAL

Below is your space to write your schedule, the goals to focus on today, mental training to do, plans for the future, struggles you're going through or how you're feeling. You can write anything you want!

REFLECTIONS

What went well?

What did I learn today?

What actions will I take now, based on what I have learnt?

RATINGS FOR TODAY

Give yourself a score from 0-10 on the scales below on how well you did in these areas:

VALUES

0 10

How well did I live as "the person I wanted to be?"

EFFORT

0 10

How hard did I try?

COURAGE

0 10

How brave was I?

DATE: ______________________

What things can I be grateful for today?

How will I be courageous today?

What values can I focus on today?

JOURNAL

Below is your space to write your schedule, the goals to focus on today, mental training to do, plans for the future, struggles you're going through or how you're feeling. You can write anything you want!

REFLECTIONS

What went well?

What did I learn today?

What actions will I take now, based on what I have learnt?

RATINGS FOR TODAY

Give yourself a score from 0-10 on the scales below on how well you did in these areas:

VALUES

0 10

How well did I live as "the person I wanted to be?"

EFFORT

0 10

How hard did I try?

COURAGE

0 10

How brave was I?

DATE:

What things can I be grateful for today?

How will I be courageous today?

What values can I focus on today?

JOURNAL

Below is your space to write your schedule, the goals to focus on today, mental training to do, plans for the future, struggles you're going through or how you're feeling. You can write anything you want!

REFLECTIONS

What went well?

What did I learn today?

What actions will I take now, based on what I have learnt?

RATINGS FOR TODAY

Give yourself a score from 0-10 on the scales below on how well you did in these areas:

VALUES

0 10

How well did I live as "the person I wanted to be?"

EFFORT

0 10

How hard did I try?

COURAGE

0 10

How brave was I?

DATE:____________________________

What things can I be grateful for today?

How will I be courageous today?

What values can I focus on today?

JOURNAL

Below is your space to write your schedule, the goals to focus on today, mental training to do, plans for the future, struggles you're going through or how you're feeling. You can write anything you want!

REFLECTIONS

What went well?

What did I learn today?

What actions will I take now, based on what I have learnt?

RATINGS FOR TODAY

Give yourself a score from 0-10 on the scales below on how well you did in these areas:

VALUES

0 10

How well did I live as "the person I wanted to be?"

EFFORT

0 10

How hard did I try?

COURAGE

0 10

How brave was I?

DATE: ____________________

What things can I be grateful for today?

How will I be courageous today?

What values can I focus on today?

JOURNAL

Below is your space to write your schedule, the goals to focus on today, mental training to do, plans for the future, struggles you're going through or how you're feeling. You can write anything you want!

REFLECTIONS

What went well?

What did I learn today?

What actions will I take now, based on what I have learnt?

RATINGS FOR TODAY

Give yourself a score from 0-10 on the scales below on how well you did in these areas:

VALUES

0 10

How well did I live as "the person I wanted to be?"

EFFORT

0 10

How hard did I try?

COURAGE

0 10

How brave was I?

"Obstacles don't have to stop you, if you run into a wall don't turn around and give up. Figure out how to climb it, go through it, work around it."

- Michael Jordan

HOW ARE THINGS GOING FOR YOU?

REFLECT ON WHAT YOU'VE ACHIEVED AND WHAT YOU'RE PROUD OF:

DATE: ______________________

What things can I be grateful for today?

How will I be courageous today?

What values can I focus on today?

JOURNAL

Below is your space to write your schedule, the goals to focus on today, mental training to do, plans for the future, struggles you're going through or how you're feeling. You can write anything you want!

REFLECTIONS

What went well?

What did I learn today?

What actions will I take now, based on what I have learnt?

RATINGS FOR TODAY

Give yourself a score from 0-10 on the scales below on how well you did in these areas:

VALUES

0 10

How well did I live as "the person I wanted to be?"

EFFORT

0 10

How hard did I try?

COURAGE

0 10

How brave was I?

DATE: ______

What things can I be grateful for today?

How will I be courageous today?

What values can I focus on today?

JOURNAL

Below is your space to write your schedule, the goals to focus on today, mental training to do, plans for the future, struggles you're going through or how you're feeling. You can write anything you want!

REFLECTIONS

What went well?

What did I learn today?

What actions will I take now, based on what I have learnt?

RATINGS FOR TODAY

Give yourself a score from 0-10 on the scales below on how well you did in these areas:

VALUES

0 10

How well did I live as "the person I wanted to be?"

EFFORT

0 10

How hard did I try?

COURAGE

0 10

How brave was I?

DATE:

What things can I be grateful for today?

How will I be courageous today?

What values can I focus on today?

JOURNAL

Below is your space to write your schedule, the goals to focus on today, mental training to do, plans for the future, struggles you're going through or how you're feeling. You can write anything you want!

REFLECTIONS

What went well?

What did I learn today?

What actions will I take now, based on what I have learnt?

RATINGS FOR TODAY

Give yourself a score from 0-10 on the scales below on how well you did in these areas:

VALUES

0 — 10

How well did I live as "the person I wanted to be?"

EFFORT

0 — 10

How hard did I try?

COURAGE

0 — 10

How brave was I?

DATE: ____________________

What things can I be grateful for today?

How will I be courageous today?

What values can I focus on today?

JOURNAL

Below is your space to write your schedule, the goals to focus on today, mental training to do, plans for the future, struggles you're going through or how you're feeling. You can write anything you want!

REFLECTIONS

What went well?

What did I learn today?

What actions will I take now, based on what I have learnt?

RATINGS FOR TODAY

Give yourself a score from 0-10 on the scales below on how well you did in these areas:

VALUES

0 10

How well did I live as "the person I wanted to be?"

EFFORT

0 10

How hard did I try?

COURAGE

0 10

How brave was I?

Made in the USA
Columbia, SC
25 April 2022